LET'S STOP FOR
TEA

1990

Produced by the Publishing Division of the Automobile
Association in association with Premier Brands (UK) Ltd.

Maps prepared by the Cartographic Department of the
Automobile Association.
© The Automobile Association 1989

Cover Illustration	Blue Chip Illustration
Feature Design	Trademark Graphics
Colour Illustrations	Maria Manlow
Black and White Illustrations	Image Box
Head of Advertisement Sales	Christopher Heard
Tel 0256 20123	
Advertisement Production	Karen Weeks
Tel 0256 20123	

Typeset by Bookworm Typesetting, Manchester
Printed and bound by Hazell, Watson and Viney, Aylesbury
Colour supplement produced by JB Shears and Sons Ltd,
Basingstoke.

A CIP catalogue record for this book is available from the British
Library.

Published by the Automobile Association, Fanum House,
Basingstoke, Hampshire RG21 2EA.

ISBN 0 86145 823 0

C O N T E N T S

Introduction

Afternoon tea is one of the great British traditions
and has been popular in these islands ever since the
leaves were first introduced in the 17th century.
Britain's fondness for 'a nice cup of tea' at any hour
of the day, but especially in the afternoon, has
survived both wartime rationing and the
competition from instant coffee. Today it is more
popular than ever before with people of all ages,
and particularly with families.

The AA, sponsored by Typhoo, one of Britain's most
popular teas, along with sister speciality blends
Melroses and Ridgways, has produced this guide to
hundreds of places throughout the country where
you can be sure of finding a good cup of tea – with
cakes and scones to match – in pleasant
surroundings. Tea places range from the grandest of
hotels to small village teashops, restaurants in busy
town centres where you can rest from shopping or
sight-seeing, or cafes in garden centres and places
of interest. So wherever you are, you shouldn't be
too far from somewhere to Stop for Tea. If you are a
motorist on a long journey, a break for refreshment
is especially important to relieve stress and
tiredness, and what better and safer 'pick-me-up'
could you find than a pot of tea?

All the places in this guide have been visited by the
AA's highly qualified team of hotel and restaurant
inspectors, who have assessed each teashop and
hotel, sampling the afternoon teas, noting the

service, surroundings and the quality of baking
which together make the British tea such an
enjoyable tradition.

We do not claim to have discovered every single
good teashop in the country, and if we have missed
your favourite local tea place, or if on your travels
you find somewhere really good that is not included
in the Guide, we should like to hear about it, so
please use the report form at the end of the book to
tell us about it.

How to use this book

The tea places in the gazetteer are listed
alphabetically by place-name throughout England,
Scotland and Wales.

For quick reference, if you are visiting an unfamiliar
area, every location represented in the guide is
shown on the appropriate map in the Atlas section.

The example of a gazetteer entry given below
should help you to make the most of the
information given.

Symbols
A number of symbols may appear in each entry:

Credit Cards:
The following credit cards may be accepted, but
check current details when booking:

1 = Access
2 = American Express
3 = Visa

Disabled access:

  ♿ This symbol shows that the establishment has
    toilets with access for the disabled.

Example of a gazeteer entry

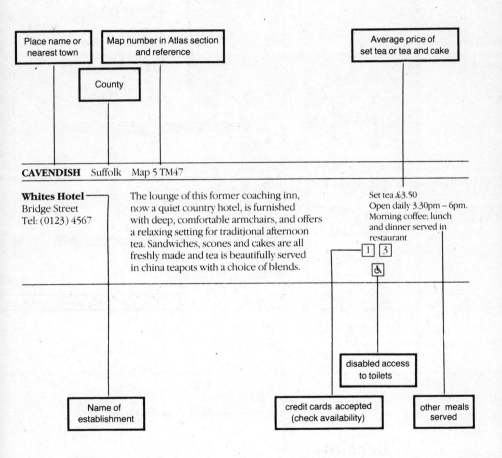

Place name or nearest town

Map number in Atlas section and reference

Average price of set tea or tea and cake

County

CAVENDISH Suffolk   Map 5 TM47

Whites Hotel
Bridge Street
Tel: (0123) 4567

The lounge of this former coaching inn, now a quiet country hotel, is furnished with deep, comfortable armchairs, and offers a relaxing setting for traditional afternoon tea. Sandwiches, scones and cakes are all freshly made and tea is beautifully served in china teapots with a choice of blends.

Set tea £3.50
Open daily 3.30pm – 6pm.
Morning coffee; lunch and dinner served in restaurant

disabled access to toilets

Name of establishment

credit cards accepted (check availability)

other meals served

Opening doors to the World of books

BOOK TOKEN

Book Tokens

Book Tokens can be bought and exchanged at most bookshops

An 18th-century tea garden as painted by George Morland

The tradition of afternoon tea.

Tea drinking is traditionally the pursuit of the British — in crisis or in celebration and not least during that hour in the afternoon when the most important thing becomes buttered scones, mouthwatering fruit cake and of course a piping hot pot of tea.

Yet the British were by no means the first Europeans to drink tea, and in its early days this new passion had so many opponents that it is a wonder it survived at all. By looking at the history and tradition of tea drinking we can begin to understand why it is still the most popular drink in Britain today.

Tea was first introduced into Europe in the middle of the sixteenth century by the Portuguese, and later the Dutch, who began regular trading in China and the Far East. It was not sold publicly in England until 1657 when Cromwell was Lord Protector, and to make it acceptable to the Puritans, tea was advertised as a drink with medicinal qualities,
"good for clearing the sight, removing difficulty in breathing, strengthening the stomach, vanquishing heavy dreams and improving the memory".

9

At first it was sold in coffee houses and was often accompanied with instructions as to how to drink this strange new beverage. The name 'Chia' by which it was sometimes known led some people to believe that it should be chewed, while others rolled the dry leaves in paper and smoked them!

Samuel Pepys recorded his first drink of tea in 1660, when he was 27,
> *"Did send for a cupp of (a China drink) Tee, which I had never drank before".*

However it did not become universally popular until the Restoration of Charles II and in particular his marriage to the Portuguese Princess, Catherine of Braganza in 1662 who brought a large chest of tea as part of her dowry.

Catherine also brought the tradition of drinking tea in the afternoon to the English court and soon the East India Company were regularly importing tea into England.

By the turn of the eighteenth century tea had become a truly 'democratic' drink, drunk by all classes, despite the fact that a pound of tea could cost up to a third of a week's wages. So precious was it that tea was usually stored in ornate locked caddies, kept not in the kitchen but in the drawing room under the watchful eye of the mistress of the house. It was not uncommon for the gentry, after brewing their own tea, to pass the leaves on to their servants who would then sell these twice-used leaves.

Tea-drinking was not only popular in the home. Several Pleasure Gardens opened on the outskirts of London where men and women of all classes would mix together, strolling along lantern-lit walks, watching fireworks and, of course, drinking tea. In America tea gardens grew up around natural springs where the water was sold as special 'tea water'.

One of the most outspoken supporters of tea-drinking was Dr Johnson who described himself as
> *"a hardened and shameless tea drinker . . . whose kettle has scarcely time to cool"*

but despite the fact that, if not through any medicinal qualities, the popularity of tea *had* brought about an improvement in the nation's health by requiring the water to be boiled, and reducing the consumption of the previously most popular beverage, gin, there were still many opponents to this new national habit.

A French Count visiting England in 1784 observed that
> *"throughout the whole of England the drinking of tea is general. You have it twice a day, and though the expense is considerable, the humblest peasant has his tea just like the rich man."*

In particular the new fashion for taking tea 'breaks' during the working day was criticised, causing the economist Arthur Young who made a tour of England in the 1770s, to warn that tea-drinking would be the downfall of the empire.

Smuggling

The popularity of tea made it a useful source of tax revenue which rose to such enormous proportions by the mid eighteenth century that the practice of smuggling began.

The universal demand for cheaper tea encouraged all sorts of people to engage in smuggling — from wealthy merchants who saw it as an acceptable part of their business — to the clergy who often allowed the crypts of their churches to be used as safe hiding places for the unlawful cargoes.

The tea came from Dutch merchant ships anchored off the English coast and was transferred by local fishermen to caves and underground passages.

Another way to profit from the high price of tea was to mix it with other leaves. A common mixture called 'smouch' consisted of a combination of tea leaves, ash leaves boiled in iron sulphate and sheep's dung. One small village in the south of England made up to 20 tons of this mixture a year.

The British government also tried to impose these high taxes on tea sold in the American colonies but American women refused to buy it and in 1773 a revolt took place when Bostonians dressed as Red Indians held their infamous Tea Party aboard a ship and unloaded £10,000 worth of tea into the sea.

The British closed the port and American revolutionary sentiments stirred. Eventually, in 1784, the taxes were reduced by Pitt the Younger from 120 per cent to 12½ per cent and smuggling was no longer necessary.

Clipper Races

America was also the birthplace of the new breed of Tea Clippers.

The first of these elegant three-masted ships to operate commercially was the *Rainbow*, launched in New York in 1845. On her second voyage, the round trip took less time than other ships took one way, and at first British vessels could not compete.

The first British-built clipper — the *Stornoway* — was launched for the traders Jardine Matheson in 1860.

Another, the *Lightning*, once averaged a speed of 18 knots — an all-time record for sailing ships and not far off the speed of a modern liner.

Clipper Races appealed to the public as an exciting sporting event, with several ships racing from the Canton river in China, round the Cape, up the Atlantic and into the Channel — where news of their sighting was reported to London.

Progress up-Channel was followed with great excitement. The clippers were towed up the River Thames by tugs and the race was not finished until chests of tea were hurled ashore at the docks with the winning cargo commanding the highest price at auction.

The most famous clipper was the *Cutty Sark* built in 1869 which can still be seen today in dry dock at Greenwich Pier.

The 'invention' of Afternoon Tea.

The very first 'Afternoon Tea' is traditionally attributed to Anna, 7th Duchess of Bedford who became tired of the 'sinking feeling' at around four o'clock in the long afternoons between lunch and a fashionably late dinner.

Her custom of ordering cake with her tea soon spread among her friends until it evolved into an elaborate ceremony for which ladies changed into elegant tea gowns and were served with many sorts of food; some of them are described on pages twenty-two and twenty-three.

Your Fate in Your Tea Cup

With so many people using teabags today we might forget that the tea leaves left in the bottom of the cup were themselves important to our tea-drinking ancestors. Indeed by the late nineteenth century the practice of fortune-telling from tea leaves was so popular that Andrew Melrose & Co. produced a small booklet which claimed to help the reader

> *"pull back the veil and predict the events which the dim future has in store for us".*

As well as interpreting the shapes or figures which might be left after revolving the tea-cup rapidly, the book also advised how to judge the qualities of a man or woman by the way they took their tea. Thus a preference for strong tea in a man might show perseverance and resoluteness, whilst in a woman it showed qualities of cheerfulness.

There were other ways of discovering your destiny. The all-important question of a future marriage partner could, apparently, be decided by selecting several tea-stalks which were 'named' after the drinker and possible candidates.

Having stirred the tea vigorously, the stalk to which your own clung was your intended spouse. But if the stalk remained alone you were not destined to marry.

For such momentous decisions the tea leaves' predictions could sometimes seem harsh and Melroses were careful to point out that if you were to choose your partner for life from your tea cup, to use a good quality tea — preferably Melroses!

Andrew Melrose

*The founder of the Melrose tea company was an Edinburgh merchant who was quick to recognise the great changes occurring in the tea trade at the turn of the nineteenth century. By the 1830s Andrew Melrose already had three shops in Edinburgh and realised the great opportunities to be had when the Charter of the East India Company expired. This ended the monopoly on trade with China and the Indies and in 1833 he chartered the **Isabella** to sail to Canton. The arrival of this cargo in Leith was the first tea to be imported into any port outside London: an ambitious project which paid handsome rewards. Andrew's son William had shown great aptitude as a tea taster and was sent to China as a buyer for the company. His regular letters back to Edinburgh shed a fascinating light on the early days of tea trading and the habits of Victorian tea drinkers. The Queen herself enjoyed tea greatly, and in 1837 Andrew Melrose & Co. received one of the first Royal Appointments of her reign.*

Thomas Ridgway

Ridgways was founded in 1836 when Thomas Ridgway opened his first teashop in the City of London. His business philosophy was one of offering "the best quality at a fair price", and his reputation for quality teas led to early success.

Throughout the 19th century the company grew rapidly, setting up its own production facilities and opening further shops across the country.

In 1886 Queen Victoria asked Ridgways to make a special blend of tea for her own personal use. This blend became known as 'Her Majesty's Blend' and is still unique to Ridgways. Queen Victoria was so delighted with the result that she gave the company the Royal Warrant which has continued to the present royal family — Ridgways currently holds Royal Warrants of Appointments to Queen Elizabeth II and the Queen Mother.

The Company also has a thriving export business which began in 1888 with the export of Her Majesty's Blend to the USA and Ridgways now trades with over 50 countries as far afield as the Middle East, Japan and Australia — where speciality tea-drinking is growing more and more popular.

Tea place of the year

While visiting many hundreds of teashops, restaurants and hotels to select those included in this guide, our AA inspectors were also searching for a particularly special Tea Place of the Year.

Of the many excellent places they found — which can all be seen in the gazetteer — the three finalists were chosen not because they are the most luxurious or famous, but because they offer a warm welcome, charming surroundings, friendly service and a delicious selection of fresh scones, cakes and sandwiches. And, of course, an excellent pot of tea!

Market Place Teashop
Barnard Castle

At the centre of the historic town of Barnard Castle — where ancient houses cluster around the walls of the ruined medieval castle — stands **Market Place Teashop**, which itself dates back to 1702.

Restored and run for the past 20 years by Bob Hilton, the teashop is full of character and charm, with low beams, stone walls and flagstones, and a roaring fire greets customers on colder days. Food is served all day, but teatime is a real treat with a wide selection of cakes which might include gâteaux, Jap cakes, fruit pies and freshly baked scones, all beautifully presented on fine china. If you enjoy trying speciality blends of tea you will find a good variety here, served from silver teapots.

Whether you've spent a strenuous day exporing the beautiful countryside of surrounding Teesdale, or taken a gentle stroll around the town where Dickens collected material for **Nicholas Nickleby**, this is an ideal place to 'Stop for Tea'.

See gazetteer entry under Barnard Castle.

The Tea Cosy
Newtonmore

Four years ago Anne Bertram decided to transform part of the small craft and book shop which she ran with her husband in Newtonmore, into a tearoom.

The result was **The Tea Cosy**, aptly named as the tiny tearoom only has three tables, with another outside in fine weather, but if you have to wait it is well worthwhile — to indulge in Anne's delicious home baking.

Fruit and wholemeal scones with cheese or homemade jam, gingerbread, shortbread and a tempting array of cakes such as coffee and walnut sponge, lemon whisky cake and banana bread, are all freshly baked and the full afternoon tea is particularly good value. A wide selection of teas includes Blue Lady and fruit infusions with passionfruit or mango and strawberry.

See gazetteer entry under Newtonmore.

Emily's at Park Hall
Charnock Richard

A lively hotel and leisure complex might be the last place that you would expect to find a traditional teashop, yet in the attractive square at the heart of Park Hall Hotel, Charnock Richard stands **Emily's**, which although only established in 1989, offers the comfortable surroundings and good service which reflect the atmosphere of a more genteel era.

Set in beautiful Lancashire countryside, Emily's is within easy reach of the M6 Motorway and many attractions including Wigan Pier, 16th-century Astley Hall and the Magical Kingdom of Camelot theme park.

Lancashire specialities such as Chorley cakes, parkin, Eccles cakes and Goosnargh cakes — butter shortbread with caraway seed — feature in the delightful menu, alongside a poem about 'Our Emily' and her motto, "Afternoon Tea is better than lunch!".

See gazetteer entry under Charnock Richard.

15

The First Teashop

The tea gardens at Vauxhall and Ranelagh had closed by the middle of the nineteenth century and there was nowhere for the tea-drinking British public to enjoy a pot of tea outside their homes until the first teashop opened in 1864. The enterprising manageress of a bakery belonging to the Aerated Bread Company invited friends and a few customers to take tea in the back of the store — then encouraged ABC to spread the practice.

Within a few years there were ABC teashops and other chains in most cities. They were particularly patronised by young working women who could at last eat out alone and inexpensively.

Taking afternoon tea also became popular in hotels, the Tea Dance was revived from the days of the London Tea Gardens, and through periods of wartime and prosperity alike, the tradition of going 'out' to tea flourished.

. . . And so it does today.

Our life-styles may have become more hectic and the packaging of tea has certainly developed to keep pace with modern life, but whether it is in a cosy teashop or the grandest hotel, continue the tradition and 'Let's Stop For Tea'.

Whether you are catching a quick bite, as in Edward Burra's evocative painting of a snack bar, or whiling away a leisurely hour, tea-drinking in the 20th century is as popular as it was 200 years ago.

John Sumner and Typhoo

The medicinal qualities of tea which had been so important when it was first introduced into England were equally important for a Birmingham grocer called John Sumner.

In 1905 he blended a new small-leaf Ceylon tea and asked his sister to try it before selling it in his store. John Sumner's sister had long suffered from a digestive disorder and when she discovered that the new tea helped her condition far more than the large-leaf variety popular at the time it was decided to call the tea after the Chinese word for "doctor". 'Typhoo' was born, and each box carried the words, 'the tea that doctors recommend'.

The new blend became so popular that in a short time families in the area who drank it became known as 'Typhoo-ites' and John Sumner's tea company became one of the most successful in the country.

Some facts and figures . . .

The tea you drink today has probably been blended from up to 30 different teas by expert tea tasters to give a brew of consistently high quality. Where does this tea come from?

 Tea is grown in more than 25 sub-tropical countries with over 25 per cent of the entire production imported by Britain.

 The tea bush needs a warm, wet climate with at least 100 centimetres of rain a year.

 New bushes are grown from cuttings and take three to five years (depending on the altitude of the Tea Estate) to mature for production.

 Young shoots are plucked every seven to fourteen days. Only the leaf bud and the top two leaves are used.

 The freshly plucked green shoots are then withered, rolled, fermented and dried before sorting into different grades according to size.

 The familiar plywood chests are still used for packing and transporting tea to auction with details of the Estate, grade and weight stencilled on the side of the chest.

Every week skilled tea buyers bid at the London tea auction rooms. They will already have inspected the tea and the blenders will have specified the types they need to produce a consistent blend. Although the bidding is rapid it is a tradition that two or three rival companies may agree to share a lot rather than force up the price artificially.

Blending

The blending of tea has often been likened to the skilled tasting of fine wines — even down to the familiar 'slurp'.

Each sample is prepared meticulously. Half a pint of fresh boiling water is poured onto 5.65 grams of tea — which is twice the quantity of a normal brew. After three minutes the brew is stirred and after six minutes the leaves are taken out.

The tea taster will then suck in a spoonful hard against the palate, taking in a lot of air, swill it around his mouth and spit it out, enabling him to get an accurate assessment of its flavour. When the result meets the stringent requirements of the blender it can be copied in bulk from a blend sheet.

In general, North Indian teas (such as Assam), are used to give strength; Ceylon, South Indian and Indonesian teas give flavour and African teas give colour.

Different parts of the tea plant also give different characteristics: the leaves give flavour while the stalks give bouquet.

You can 'test' your own tea in three stages just as a professional blender would: look at the dry leaves for size, and at the colour with and without milk. The smaller the size of the leaf the more easily it will infuse, while the colour should always be a bright coppery gold.

Packing

The final stage in the tea-producing process today is the packaging, although when tea first became fashionable in Britain there was no such thing as a tea packet and certainly not a tea bag.

For those families who could afford the luxury of tea, purchases were based on weight, with customers providing their own containers to buy small amounts of tea from the huge chests in grocers' stores. It was not until the end of the eighteenth century that grocers began providing tea in brown-paper wrappers, often as a guarantee against it being adulterated with other leaves.

Packet tea was introduced a few years later and was sold by chemists and confectioners but the tea bag itself did not appear for nearly another century. Tradition has it that it developed by

accident when a merchant sent out samples in silk bags and some customers put them straight into the cup with boiling water! The introduction of the tea bag brought a virtual revolution in tea and it has taken another 35 years for any further major developments to take place.

It is market leaders Typhoo who have found the key to this latest revolution, and this time it is in the design of the box rather than in the bag.

The familiar frustrations of trying to open a new box of tea when first the cellophane wrapper will not open and then tea dust scatters everywhere compounded by only being able to fit half of the bags in the packet into your own caddy have been recognised by Typhoo and solved in a revolutionary way.

The cellophane wrap and flimsy box have been replaced by a rigid, upright box which can easily withstand the rigours of the kitchen cupboard. A convenient tear strip allows easy opening and bags are contained in foil pouches to preserve the freshness of the tea until it is used.

Another tea revolution!

Brewing up . . .

Producing a good cup doesn't finish once it is safely packaged, but by following these guidelines from Typhoo you can be sure of a perfect cup:

1. Let the tap run for a few moments before filling the kettle — fresh water contains more oxygen and improves the taste.
2. Make sure the water is really *boiling* — to bring out the colour and flavour.
3. Heat the pot to keep the tea hot while brewing.
4. Use the right amount of tea.
5. Allow the tea to brew for about four minutes to enhance the colour and flavour.
6. Remove the bag before brewing time is up to prevent stewing.

Try a Speciality Blend

You have probably noticed that more and more teashops and hotels are serving speciality teas.

Unlike a 'standard' cup of tea, which is blended from teas from all over the world, a speciality tea must contain at least 60 per cent of tea from one specific district — giving a very distinctive taste and aroma. The more tea used from that district, the more distinctive is the taste, which is why Melrose's speciality teas contain 100 per cent pure tea from Assam, Ceylon and Darjeeling, plus the traditional favourites of Earl Grey (which is China tea scented with bergamot oil), English Breakfast (a mixture of Indian and Ceylon teas) and lemon tea.

Each speciality tea has a definite taste and is often recommended for drinking at certain times of the day. These notes on speciality blends should help you to decide which one you want to try next.

Melroses Pure Assam

Picked solely from the Assam area of Northern India, this tea is strong and full-bodied, giving a particularly refreshing 'pick up' tea.

Melroses Pure Ceylon

Pure Ceylon teabags contain a superb blend of high-grown Ceylon tea from around the city of Kandy. The delightful golden colour and delicate flavour make this an ideal mid-morning drink or a refreshing drink after a heavy lunch.

Melroses Pure Darjeeling

Darjeeling teas give a delicate aroma — known as the 'champagne of teas'. A perfect accompaniment to a light afternoon tea.

Melroses Earl Grey

The finest Chinese leaf tea is carefully scented with bergamot oil to produce the distinctive flavour, said to be named after the Second Earl Grey. Drink it with, or without, milk.

Melroses English Breakfast

A refreshing blend of choice Indian and Ceylon teas giving a typically 'British' cup of tea which can be drunk at any time of the day.

Extra Special

Speciality teas are also very versatile, and fruit flavours can blend particularly well to make a delicious punch for special occasions.

Plantation Punch *(serves 12)*

1 litre (1¾ pint) freshly brewed Melroses Assam Tea
1 litre (1¾ pint) medium sweet cider
50g (2oz) sugar
100g (4oz) Kumquats (a small citrus fruit)
6 cloves
Blade mace.

Put the tea, cider and sugar in a coated or stainless steel pan. Slice the Kumquats, leaving six whole. Press a clove into each of the whole fruit and add to the pan together with the blade mace. Heat gently just below simmering for at least an hour.
Serve piping hot.
A slow cooker is ideal.

Summer Sip *(serves 10)*

700ml (1¼ pint) chilled Melroses Earl Grey Tea
1 punnet strawberries, thinly sliced
Frozen honeydew melon balls
70cl bottle sparkling perry or white wine
Crushed ice.

Put the tea, strawberries and half the melon balls into a punch bowl. Stand for at least an hour.
Just before serving, stir in the chilled wine, remaining melon balls and crushed ice.
The delicate flavour of these summer fruits mingles with the distinctive flavouring of the Earl Grey Tea to give a light and refreshing summer punch.

Iced Tea

Increasingly popular during the summer months, iced tea can be made with your favourite blend by infusing with cold water for at least an hour. This will ensure that the tea remains clear, as hot water may cloud on cooling. After straining the tea, pour into ice-filled glasses and add a sprig of mint or slice of lemon for a long, refreshing drink.

Tea-Time Treats

It would be difficult to stop for tea without trying some of the tempting tea-time treats that go with it. But just as tea-drinking has a history, so many of these foods also have long traditions.

The Sandwich is quite literally the namesake of the fourth Earl of Sandwich who, in 1762, was having a particularly successful evening at cards. So good was his hand that when he became hungry he could not bear to break off for a meal. He whispered his request to his servant who returned with a hunk of beef between two slices of bread. That night after eating the first sandwich, the Earl is reputed to have won £10,000.

One of the most popular varieties, still, is the cucumber sandwich which dates from Victorian times when afternoon tea had become altogether more genteel. The bread must be wafer thin and, ideally, crustless.

Dundee Cake was originally named after the Dundee marmalade which was used in the recipe in the eighteenth century. Today candied peel and other citrus fruits are included as a reminder of the past.

Eccles Cakes

The Lancashire town of Eccles takes its name from an old word for 'church'. The Eccles cake dates back many hundreds of years and was originally made in the town on religious feast days. The Puritans, however, decided they were too rich and delicious — and probably a bad influence on the good people of Eccles — and so a law was passed in 1650 which meant that you could be sent to prison for eating an Eccles cake.

Fortunately no such law exists today!

Gingerbread

Gingerbread is one of the world's oldest 'cakes'. Originally the recipe included honey, flavoured with claret, liquorice and pepper. Gingerbread was 'gilded' for religious feasts, rolled and cut into the shapes of saints and princes — hence today's penchant for gingerbread men.

Victoria Sandwich

Sponge cakes were not introduced into English kitchens until the end of the eighteenth century, when it became possible to maintain the constant oven temperature essential to their success. However, in those days the eggs were beaten with a bunch of birch twigs or a simple fork and recipes recommended egg-beating for up to three hours.

The Victoria Sandwich was named in honour of Queen Victoria who was a great believer in the restorative power of afternoon tea.

Devon and Cornwall 'Splits'

Because of the strong dairy-farming influence in the West Country, cream was traditionally used in baking, much as we might use butter today. The favourite way of using cream however, was to 'sandwich' together the 'splits' of light dough with jam, or to spread on scones or Sally Lunns — the latter being the famous cakes originating in a bakery in Bath where they are still made today.

The rich mixture of a 'split' filled with clotted cream and treacle is known in Cornwall as 'Thunder and Lightning'. Devon Splits are smaller than Cornish ones and may be known as 'Cutrands' or 'Chudleighs' after the town of that name.

The Birth of the Teapot

As the passion for tea drinking grew in the eighteenth century so did the demand for its associated 'paraphernalia'.

If Chinese porcelain or silverware were too expensive, then teapots could be bought in pewter or Dutch Delftware. In the middle of the eighteenth century, soft-paste porcelain, decorated with flowers and fables, was introduced at Chelsea. Competition came from Bow with their oriental scenes in blue and white and from Worcester where the art of intricate gilding was perfected.

One man who undoubtedly did much to popularise tea-drinking was Josiah Wedgwood, who produced tea services at deliberately low prices so that even the poorest families could take part in the 'tea ceremony'. The early designs were simple earthenware, with many teapots in the shape of animals, and Wedgwood later went on to produce his attractive 'creamware', also cheaper than porcelain, whose popularity was greatly boosted when Queen Charlotte purchased a set.

The Victorians invented many elaborate additions to their tea services including the two-spouted teapot for two brews of different strengths, and moustache cups with a small ledge inside the rim on which a gentleman's moustache could be rested whilst drinking!

As the ceremony of afternoon tea became more involved, so the tea service grew to include side plates, cake stands, milk jugs and sugar bowls. Another influential company was Josiah Spode who introduced a bone porcelain so fine that you could see the shadows of your fingers through it.

Most of the factories producing tea services were in the Midlands, and the name for that region became 'The Potteries'.

"What a part of confidante has that poor tea pot played ever since the kindly plant was introduced among us!" Thackeray, writing in the 19th century, reflects the rise in popularity of tea-drinking. This cabbage-leaf teapot is an example of the more homely style of pottery introduced by Josiah Wedgwood's firm.

ABBERLEY   Hereford and Worcester   Map 07 SO76

The Elms Tel (0299) 896666	This lovely Queen Anne house has just gone through a major refurbishment, and the three lounges are lovelier than ever with an inviting array of deep seating. Formal teas are available throughout the year, but are particularly pleasant during the summer within sight of the lovely grounds – 12 acres of well-kept gardens and lawns. There is a selection of very good teas and a refreshing infusion of fresh peppermint leaves. Scones, cakes and biscuits and The Elms' own rich fruitcake are all made on the premises, and locally grown strawberries and cream are available in season.	Pot of tea 85p, full afternoon tea £6.50 Open all year, every day, 3 – 6pm (for afternoon tea) Meals available $\boxed{1}$ $\boxed{2}$ $\boxed{3}$ $\boxed{\xi}$

ABBERLEY   Hereford and Worcester   Map 07 SO76

Manor Arms at Abberley Tel (0299) 896507	This is a charming country inn standing in the centre of old Abberley Village. The pleasant and efficient staff serve good tea, and there is a selection of sandwiches and homemade cakes, biscuits and scones.	Set tea £4.50 Open Apr – Oct, every day, 3 – 5pm $\boxed{1}$ $\boxed{2}$ $\boxed{3}$

ABBOTSBURY   Dorset   Map 03 SY68

Ilchester Arms Tel (0305) 871243	Set in the centre of Abbotsbury village, the Ilchester Arms is an old coaching inn with comfortable lounges, and a conservatory restaurant with garden-style furniture. Homemade cakes and scones are served.	Cream tea £2.20 Open all year, every day, 2.30 – 5.30pm (for afternoon tea) $\boxed{1}$ $\boxed{3}$

ABERDARE   Mid Glamorgan   Map 03 S000

Sirvini's Restaurant 2 Cardiff Street Tel (0685) 873351	Located in the town centre of Aberdare, this restaurant on two levels serves a wide variety of pastries, cakes and pies, and there are cakes and bread on sale at the counter. Speciality ice cream is available.	Tea 40p Open all year, Mon – Sat, 8am – 5.45pm Lunches and snacks available

---

ABERDARON   Gwynedd   Map 06 SH12

Hen Blas Crafts
Tel (075886) 438

A delightful little teashop/café is set at the back of this interesting craft and gift shop. A traditional Welsh dresser displays an array of homemade cake – bara brith, chocolate cakes, rum and fruit cakes and Nelson cake. Smoking is not permitted.

Pot of tea 55p
Open Easter – Oct, every day, 9am – 6pm
Lunches served
[1] [3]

ABERDEEN   Grampian   *Aberdeenshire*   Map 15 NJ90

Coffee Club
Bruce Miller and Co
363 Union Street
Tel (0224) 592211

This attractive restaurant serves light snacks and teas at the rear of the first floor of this book and music shop. There is a tempting range of home-baked scones, cakes, pancakes and biscuits displayed on the tea trolleys, and a choice of tea blends is available.

Pot of tea 55p
Open all year, Mon – Sat, 9.30am – 4.45pm
Lunches and snacks available
[1] [3]

ABERDEEN   Grampian   *Aberdeenshire*   Map 15 NJ90

Music Hall Coffee Shop
Union Street
Tel (0224) 632080

Two rooms of the recently refurbished Music Hall provide spacious and elegant surroundings for afternoon tea. Scones, cakes, gâteaux and biscuits are supplied by local bakers, and there is a choice of Assam, Earl Grey or Darjeeling teas. Tea dances are held in the Music Hall itself every fortnight (except in the summer).

Pot of tea 60p, set afternoon tea £2.50
Open all year, Mon – Sat, 9am – 5pm
[1] [2] [3] [&]

ABERDOVEY   Gwynedd   Map 06 SN69

Old Coffee Shop
New Street
Tel (065472) 652

In a side street just off the promenade at Aberdovey is this excellent little coffee shop – full of character and offering a friendly welcome. There is a choice of tea blends, and a lovely display of home baking (the scones had just come out of the oven when our inspector arrived). The tempting menu includes light snacks and cold platters.

Pot of tea 50p, speciality teas 75p
Open Feb – Dec (closed 2 weeks in Nov), every day 10am – 5pm in summer, 10am – 6pm in winter
Hot meals available

ABERFELDY   Tayside   *Perthshire*   Map 14 NN84

Country Fare
Bridgend
Tel (0887) 20729

This popular little coffee house-cum-restaurant is conveniently located in the main street of Aberfeldy. The emphasis is on home baking – tempting offerings include wholemeal cakes and scones, flapjacks, shortbread and cream cakes. There is a choice of tea blends, and the staff are friendly and helpful. The menu also offers freshly-made quiches, meat and fish dishes and a super salad bowl.

Pot of tea 50p
Open mid Feb – Dec, Mon – Sat, 10am – 5pm

ABERLOUR Grampian *Banffshire* Map 15 NJ24

The Old Pantry The Square Tel (03405) 617	This is an attractive cottage-style restaurant with a beamed ceiling. Blue and white checked tablecloths, live fire, tiled floor and everything immaculate and orderly make this an inviting prospect for afternoon tea. There is a range of homemade scones, cakes and biscuits and a choice of tea blends.	Pot of tea 45p Open all year, Sun – Thu 9am – 6pm, Fri – Sat 9am – 9pm Lunches available

ABERNETHY Tayside *Perthshire* Map 11 NO11

Pitblae Cottage Tearoom Tel (073885) 361	Dating from the 18th century, this old building, with its timbered ceiling and rough stone walls, has been made into a homely little cottage tearoom. There are pretty tablecloths on the tables, and newspapers and magazines for customers to read. Drop scones, shortbread, Vienna shortcake, fruit slice, fairy cakes and biscuits are among the range of good home-baking available.	Pot of tea 40p Open Mar – mid Jan, Mon – Sat 10am – 5pm, Sun 12.30 – 6pm Meals and take-away service

ABERYSTWYTH Dyfed Map 06 SN58

Pennau Coffee Shop Rhydypennau Bow Street Tel (0970) 820050	A good selection of Welsh and English craftwork is on sale at the Pennau Craft and Coffee Shop. The coffee shop is attractively furnished, with cushioned cane chairs, and there is a selection of homemade scones, pastries, pies and sandwiches.	Tea 25p Open all year, Tue – Sun, 10am – 5.30pm

ABERYSTWYTH Dyfed Map 06 SN58

Welsh Fudge Shop Sandmarsh Cottage Queens Road Tel (0970) 612721	This small tearoom forms part of the Welsh Fudge Shop and is a must for anyone with a sweet tooth. All sorts of cakes and scones are served with a good pot of tea. The atmosphere is friendly.	Pot of tea 50p Open all year, Mon – Sat 8.30am – 6pm, Sun 12 – 6pm

ALFRISTON East Sussex Map 05 TQ50

Toucans Family Restaurant Tel (0323) 870234	Toucans forms part of the Drusillas Park and Zoo which includes the Adventure Playland and other family attractions. As well as home-baked cakes and scones and Sussex cream teas (with a choice of blends), Toucans children's menu offers 'jungle juice'.	Pot of tea, 70p, Sussex cream tea £1.85 Open all year, every day (except Christmas), 10.30am – 6pm Meals available

ALSTON   Cumbria   Map 12 NY74

Brownside Coach House
Tel (0498) 81263

This old rustic-style coach house dates from 1689, and from the attractive, beamed interior are views of the south Tyne valley and the Pennines. Good home baking is accompanied by a friendly homely welcome from Mrs Graham, the proprietress.

Pot of tea 40p, set afternoon tea £2
Open Easter – early Oct, Wed – Mon, 10am – 6pm

ALSTONEFIELD   Derbyshire   Map 07 SK14

Old Post Office Tea Room
Alstonefield, Nr Ashbourne
Tel (033527) 201

This homely little cafe adjoins the village post-office, and is furnished with great charm in a mixture of styles. An interesting assortment of bric à brac and locally made preserves is displayed for sale. The teas are very good value, and the atmosphere is friendly. At weekends and holidays, three kinds of set tea are served from 3.45pm onwards, and on other days there is a selection of scones, cakes and pastries.

Pot of tea 65p, Cakes 45 – 75p, afternoon tea £2.60, egg tea £3.20
Open Mar – Nov daily except Wed and Fri, 10.30am – 5pm, set teas served only at weekends and holidays, from 3.45pm

AMBLESIDE   Cumbria   Map 07 NY30

Sheila's Cottage
The Slack
Tel (053 94) 33079

This delightful restaurant, in a charming Lakeland stone cottage, is deservedly popular with visitors to the Lakes and local customers alike. In the afternoon the friendly staff and owners Stewart and Janice Greaves serve a wide range of delicious cakes including lemon bread with lemon cheese, spicy bara brith and fresh muffins made with flour ground locally at Muncaster Mill in Eskdale. Swiss food is another speciality of Sheila's Cottage; why not try a Swiss drinking chocolate served with Jersey cream with a slice of rum-flavoured Sachertorte?

Borrowdale teabread 80p
Open Feb – Dec, Mon – Sat, 10.30am – 5.30pm
Lunches (booking advisable)

APPLEBY-IN-WESTMORLAND   Cumbria   Map 12 NY62

Courtyard Gallery
32 Boroughgate
Tel (07653) 51638

Tucked away down a passageway in Appleby is the Courtyard Gallery, which sells original paintings, pottery, glass, jewellery, turned wood and cards. At one end of the gallery, the teashop, overlooking an attractive garden, offers a selection of cakes and biscuits and a wide choice of tea blends and herb teas. No smoking is permitted.

Pot of tea 35p
Open all year (except 2 weeks in Jan), Tue – Sun 10am – 5pm, Sun 10.30am – 5pm
[1]

APPLEBY-IN-WESTMORLAND   Cumbria   Map 12 NY62

Victorian Pantry
9 Bridge Street
Tel (07683) 52593

In this attractive licensed restaurant, pleasant and efficient service by waitress in long skirts add to the Victorian atmosphere. There is a selection of cakes and scones, and the selection of tea blends includes a 'Lakeland special'.

Pot of tea 45p – 65p,
cream tea £1.10
Open all year, every day
(except Oct – Easter
closed Thu), 10am – 5pm
Restaurant meals served

ARDERSIER   Highlands   *Inverness-shire*   Map 14 NH75

The Old Bakehouse
73 High Street
Tel (0667) 62920

This teashop is an old converted bakehouse – now with a conservatory extension, and an inviting place for tea with prints on the walls, pot plants, and pine tables and chairs. There is a good selection of scones, cakes and pastries, and tea blends available include Earl Grey, jasmine and Scottish breakfast. Smoking is not permitted.

Set tea £2.20
Open May – Oct, every
day, 10am – 6pm

ASHBOURNE   Derbyshire   Map 07 SK14

**Ashbourne
Gingerbread Shop**
26 St John Street
Tel (0335) 43227

This historic half-timbered building stands in the centre of town and is almost always packed out with customers eager to sample the excellent cakes and pastries freshly made in the bakery adjoining the teashop. Gingerbread men are, naturally, a speciality but all the cakes are popular. There are six different blends of tea, and some herbal fruit teas.

Cream tea £1.80
Open Mon – Sat but not
bank holidays 8.30am –
5pm

ASHFORD   Kent   Map 05 TR04

Eastwell Manor
Eastwell Park
Boughton Lees
Tel (0233) 35751,
635751

This charming country house hotel is set in 3,000 acres of private parkland and offers much character and comfort. Afternoon tea may be taken in the delightful lounge, and service is very good and extremely efficient. Traditional full afternoon teas are available, as well as Kentish cream teas, and there is a choice of blends, served in beautiful silver teapots. This is an excellent place for a leisurely tea in luxurious surroundings.

Pot of tea £1, full
afternoon tea £5.25
Open all year, every day,
all day
Meals available
| 1 | 2 | 3 |

AVIEMORE   Highlands   *Inverness-shire*   Map 14 NH81

Chinwags Coffee Shop
Red McGregor Hotel
Main Road
Tel (0479) 810256

This smart, modern coffee shop is conveniently located off the Foyer lounge of the Red McGregor Hotel in the centre of Aviemore. There is a selection of scones, croissants, tarts, cookies, cheesecakes and gâteaux, all made on the premises.

Cakes 20p – £1.30
Open all year, every day,
9.30am – 6pm

BAGSHOT   Surrey   Map 04 SU96

Pennyhill Park
College Ride
Tel (0276) 71774

This stately English country manor house has been tastefully converted for use as a popular and elegant hotel. Afternoon tea can be taken either in the lounge or the conservatory; the staff are very smart and efficient. A choice of tea blends is offered, as well as home-baked scones, sandwiches, fresh fruit tarts and fruit cakes – an excellent prospect for tea.

Pot of tea and biscuits £2,
Latymer full tea £6.95
Open all year, every day,
tea during the afternoon
Meals available

BAKEWELL   Derbyshire   Map 08 SK26

Byways
Water Lane
Tel (062981) 812807

Quite a steep staircase leads to spacious premises for afternoon tea – there are three separate rooms, all with polished wooden tables and chairs, and the occasional sofa. Friendly staff add to a homely atmosphere. Good strong brew tea is provided, as well as homemade cakes, pastries, tarts and scones.

Pot of tea 48p – 60p,
afternoon tea £2.10
Open all year (except Christmas), Mon – Sat
10am – 5pm, Sun 1.30 – 5pm

BAKEWELL   Derbyshire   Map 08 SK26

Marguerite and Stephanie's Coffee Shop
John Sinclair
The Square
Tel (062981) 4164

Located on the first floor of Sinclair's China Shop, the coffee shop is bright, clean and spacious, with pretty floral tablecloths providing a splash of colour. A wide variety of tea blends is offered, and tea is presented in a china tea service on a silver platter. The Bakewell pudding and various cakes, pastries and biscuits are all baked on the premises.

Pot of tea 60p
Open all year, Mon – Sat
9am – 4.45pm (Thur 4pm), Sun 2 – 5pm
Light lunches and hot snacks available

BALA   Gwynedd   Map 06 SA93

Sospan-fach
97 High Street
Tel (0678) 520396

This small restaurant-cum-teashop is situated in the main street of Bala. A low beamed ceiling and open fireplace with hanging copper pans add to the character, and a local lady provides quick and friendly service.

Pot of tea 50p, set tea
£2.60
Open all year, summer
8am – 8pm (closes at
5.30pm Mon), winter
9.30am – 5.30pm
Snacks and meals
available

BALA   Gwynedd   Map 06 SA93

Y Radell
81 High Street
Tel (0678) 520203

Our inspector found a warm Welsh welcome at this small bow-fronted restaurant. Inside, the walls are adorned with bric-a-brac, there are stick-back chairs and the tables are covered with lace cloths. The homemade cakes are tempting, and the tea has a good flavour. No smoking is permitted.

Pot of tea for 1 or 2 – 70p
Open all year, every day,
9am – 5pm
Breakfast, lunches and
snacks available

1

BAMBURGH   Northumbria   Map 12 NU13

**The Copper Kettle
Tea Room**
21 Front Street
Tel (06684) 315

This is an interesting little cottage tearoom with some fine carved wood panelling and an attractive display counter adding to the period styling and character. There is a wide choice of speciality teas, herbal infusions and fruit teas, as well as a selection of homemade cakes, pastries and scones. A range of sweets, biscuits and preserves are on sale. Smoking is not permitted.

Pot of tea 45p – 55p
Open all year (restricted
service and times Nov –
Feb), every day, 10.30am –
5.30pm
Hot and cold meals and
snacks available, take-away
snacks

BAMBURGH   Northumbria   Map 12 NU13

Ramblers
5 Lucker Road
Tel (06684) 229

A homely atmosphere and friendly service are a feature of this small family-run tearoom. There is a choice of tea blends, and a selection of gâteaux, cakes, scones and sandwiches. Two rooms are available for guests taking tea.

Pot of tea 40p – 45p
Open all year, every day,
10am – 5.30pm
Meals and snacks available

1   3

BANCHORY   Grampian   *Kincardineshire*   Map 15 NO69

Banchory Lodge
Tel (03302) 2625

Delightfully situated in 12 acres of grounds along the River Dee, Banchory Lodge has a wonderful atmosphere that makes guests feel completely at ease. The owners, Dugald and Maggie Jaffrey, who have run the hotel for over 20 years, are enthusiastic about antiques, and Edwardian and Victorian pieces grace the beautiful house, along with the lovely furnishings and fresh flowers. The elegant lounges provide the perfect setting for a relaxing tea, with good-natured staff ensuring an informal and warm hospitality. Homemade cakes, shortbread, scones and freshly-cut finger sandwiches are some of the offerings for afternoon tea.

Afternoon tea £5
Open Feb – Dec, every
day, 3 – 5pm for afternoon
tea
Meals available

 1   2   3

BANCHORY   Grampian   *Kincardineshire*   Map 15 NO69

Raemoir
Tel (03302) 4884

The panelled morning room, dating from 1817, is the setting for afternoon tea here. The beautiful furnishings are complemented by lovely views over the 3,500-acre estate, and the informal and relaxing atmosphere makes a visit here an experience to remember. Homemade cakes and chef's pancakes are among the offerings for tea, as well as a choice of tea blends and herbal infusions.

Teas approximately £2.50
Open 3.30 – 5pm (for afternoon tea)
Meals available
① ② ③

BANFF   Grampian   *Banffshire*   Map 15 NJ66

George Ellis Coffee Shop
69 High Street
Tel (02612) 24042

The small coffee shop here is located at the back of the first floor of the chemist's shop. The service is pleasant, and there is a good range of homemade cakes, scones and biscuits on the trolley.

Tea 40p
Open all year, Mon – Sat (but closed Wed afternoon), 9am – 4.30pm
Light snacks available at lunchtime

BARMOUTH   Gwynedd   Map 06 SH61

Kith 'n Kin
King Edward Street
Tel (0341) 281071

This teashop is part of a well-established family bakery located on the main street near the railway station. There is a bright, fresh, friendly atmosphere here. The bakery supplies a good range of cakes, and a very good locally-made bara brith is served.

Tea 42p
Open all year, Thu – Tue, 9am – 4.30pm

BARMOUTH   Gwynedd   Map 06 SH61

The Old Tea Rooms
Church Street
Tel (0341) 280194

In the main street of Barmouth, this double-fronted teashop has plenty of character. There are padded stick-back chairs, lace cloths on the tables, and a large model of a tea clipper boat is on display. A selection of tea blends is offered, and there is a cake display and a good homemade bara brith. Smoking is not permitted.

Pot of tea 43p – 50p
Open seasonally (limited opening in winter), every day, 10.30am – 5.30pm
Light lunches available

BARNARD CASTLE   Co Durham   Map 12 NZ01

The Market Place Teashop
29 The Market Place
Tel (8033) 690110

Oak tables, low beams, stone walls, flagstone floors and an open fire when it is chilly all add to the charm and character of this wonderful little town-centre tearoom. Offerings include Jap cakes, a variety of fresh cream cakes, gâteaux and pastries; teacakes, biscuits, scones and fruit pies. There is a good variety of tea blends, served in silver teapots (and silver hot-water jugs) with Wedgwood china tea service. Staff are always friendly and attentive. This is a really excellent teashop that gives great value for money.

Pot of tea 90p
Open all year, every day (except Jan – Mar closed Sun), 10am (Sun 3pm) – 5.30pm
Varied menu available all day

BASILDON   Essex   Map 05 TQ78

Café Metro
Allders
East Gate Shopping Centre
Tel (0268) 527858

There is a feeling of France about the Café Metro, with all the atmosphere of a pavement café, pot plants and trees and soft lighting. Scones, rolls, croissants and various pastries are available, as well as a very good choice of tea blends and herbal teas.

Pot of tea 55p – 60p
Open all year (except Christmas), Mon – Sat, 10am – 7.30pm

BASILDON   Essex   Map 05 TQ78

Oliver's
54 Town Square
Tel (0268) 280886

Oliver's is a modern hot bread and coffee shop, with counter service on the ground floor and additional seating upstairs. Home-baked items include cream cakes, jam doughnuts, scones, hot buns and pastries.

Pot of tea 50p, cakes 35p – 75p
Open all year, Mon – Sat, 8.45am – 5.45pm

BASLOW   Derbyshire   Map 08 SK27

Cavendish Hotel
Tel (024688) 2311

The Cavendish is set in this Peak District village on the edge of the Chatsworth estate. Afternoon tea is a new venture here: teas are taken in the 'Garden Room', which commands superb views across part of the estate. A choice of tea blends is served in silver teapots, with Wedgwood china and linen napkins. There is a range of cakes crumpets and scones, and many items include homemade bread.

Set afternoon tea from £2
Open all year, every day, 12 noon – 6pm

BASLOW   Derbyshire   Map 08 SK27

Crofters Restaurant and Tea Room
Goose Green
Eaton Hill
Tel (0246) 883164

Morning coffees and afternoon teas are an event in this little cottage-style restaurant in the heart of Baslow village. Stone walls and coal-effect fires are a feature of the interior. A local baker supplies fruit pies, scones and various pastries.

Pot of tea 55p
Open all year, Tues – Sun, 11am – 5pm

BATH   Avon   Map 03 ST76

The Canary
3 Queens Street
Tel (0225) 24846

Tucked away on a cobbled back street in Bath, the Canary is a charming place – the décor is simple, with prints on the walls and circular bare-topped tables and wheel-back chairs. There is a wonderful display of home-baked cakes – teacakes and tea breads, wholemeal scones, merangues, fruit tartlets, cakes and pastries. The menu offers a choice of over 40 teas and 10 coffees, and provides informative and entertaining reading. There are ranges of Celon, China, India, Assam, Darjeeling and Formosa teas; a selection of blends (including 'Canary Blend' and 'Tea of the Week') as well as many herbal, exotic and fruit teas and infusions. Packets of speciality teas are on sale.

Pot of tea from 85p, clotted cream tea £2.50
Open all year, every day, 9am – 5pm (8am – 8pm in summer)
Lunches served

BATH   Avon   Map 03 ST76

Charlotte's Patisserie
Collonade Shopping Centre
Bath Street
Tel (0225) 445895

On the lower ground floor of the new Colonnade shopping centre, Charlotte's has a bright, modern décor, and a mouthwatering display of cakes and pastries. The young staff are quick and friendly and serve a wide range of teas and snacks. Specialist items are baked by the company's own local bakery.

Pot of tea from 80p, set cream tea from £2.25
Open all year, Mon – Sat, 9am – 5.30pm

BATH   Avon   Map 03 ST76

David's
17 Pulteney Bridge
Tel (0225) 464636

In a unique location, this tiny building is built on Pulteney Bridge and has views of the river and the weir beneath. Its charm is helped by very friendly and hard-working staff. A good range of interesting cakes are available – all baked by the staff, and there is a good range of interesting teas served in china pots.

Pot of tea 85p, cream tea £2.25
Open all year, Tue – Sat, 9am – 5pm
Breakfast, lunch and dinner available

BATH   Avon   Map 03 ST76

The Francis Hotel
Queen Square
Tel (0225) 24257

The Francis Hotel faces an attractive little park, and is only a stone's throw from the little narrow shopping streets that are a feature of Bath. Formal teas are taken in the lounge, and are an attraction for residents and visitors alike. There is a choice of tea blends, and sandwiches, scones, gâteaux and fruit tarts are all home-baked.

Cream tea £3.25
Open all year, every day,
3.30 – 5.30pm (for
afternoon tea)

1 2 3

BATH   Avon   Map 03 ST76

No 5 Argyle Street
Restaurant
5 Argyle Street
Tel (0225) 444499

Indoor plants, ceiling fans and cane furniture help to create a stylish atmosphere – a fun place to eat any time of day. There is a choice of tea blends. The selection of cakes includes scones, chocolate cake, cookies and brownies.

Pot of tea 50p, scones and
clotted cream £1.65
Open all year, every day,
10am – 10pm (closes 5pm
Sun)
Breakfast and lunch
available

1 2 3

BATH   Avon   Map 03 ST76

The Priory Hotel
Weston Road
Tel (0225) 331922

Surprisingly, although little more than half a mile from the bustle of Bath, the Priory is everything one expects from a country house hotel. Afternoon tea can be taken in one of the sitting rooms, or, weather permitting, on the terrace overlooking the lovely mature garden. There is a choice of tea blends, and a good range of cakes – all baked on the premises.

Set afternoon tea from £3
Open 3 – 6pm (for
afternoon tea)
Meals available

1 2 3

BATH   Avon   Map 03 ST76

The Pump Room
Tel (0225) 444477

In 1786 the present Pump Room replaced a smaller house, and ever since then this has been a favourite Bath meeting place. Elegant portraits of early dignitaries adorn the walls, chandeliers hang from the ceiling, and sedan and Bath chairs are on display. Teatime favourites here are Cobb's original Bath buns, plain and cheese scones, dark chocolate cake, fancy cakes and pastries, and toast and 'gentlemen's relish'. A selection of tea blends is available. Occasionally a musical ensemble plays for guests, making afternoon tea even more enjoyable.

'Club Tea' £3.50
Open all year, every day,
9am – 5pm (10am –
4.30pm Nov – Feb)

BATH　Avon　Map 03 ST76

Royal Crescent Hotel
16 Royal Crescent
Tel (0225) 319090

Superbly set in the middle of Bath's most famous street, the Royal Crescent offers a splendid afternoon tea in luxurious surroundings. The interior has been modernised, but there is still plenty of period charm and atmosphere – with beautiful antiques, fine paintings, delicate porcelain and lovely soft furnishings. Afternoon tea is served in three of the hotel's pleasant lounges. There is a wide choice of different tea blends, served with china service. Traditional teas include assorted finger sandwiches, scones with Jersey cream, hot buttered teacakes and – of course – Bath buns.

High tea from £6
Open all year, every day, 3 – 5pm (for afternoon tea)
Meals available
⊡1 ⊡2 ⊡3

BATH　Avon　Map 03 ST76

Sally Lunn's House
4 North Parade Passage
Tel (0225) 461634

Sally Lunn's house must have a claim to being the original tearoom from which all others followed. It is reputedly the oldest house in Bath (excavations have revealed Roman occupation) where, in 1680, Sally Lunn created her much-copied bun – a renowned delicacy. The present owners, Mike and Angela Overton, have done much to make a visit here interesting by opening the original cellars and excavations. However, this is a serious place to come and eat a piece of history. The rich, generous Sally Lunn bun can be served in countless ways – toasted and buttered, filled with sweet jam, cream or butters; with a savory filling and accompanied by salad it can make a meal. All items here are home-baked, mostly based on the brioche-like bun. A choice of tea blends is available. Smoking is not permitted.

Pot of tea from 60p, Sally Lunn bun from 98p
Open all year, every day, 10am (12 noon Sun) – 6pm
Light meals based on Sally Lunn bun

BATH　Avon　Map 03 ST76

La Silhouette
7 Green Street
Tel (0225) 460463

Plain woodchip décor, round bare-topped tables, wicker chairs and fresh flowers on the table greet guests to La Silhouette. Cakes – made on the premises – include tea cakes, scones, gâteaux, various slices and Danish pastries. There is a good selection of different tea blends.

Pot of tea 70p
Open all year, every day (but occasionally closed Sun in winter), 9am – 5.30pm (Sat 6pm), 11am – 5.30pm Sun

---

BATTLE   East Sussex   Map 05 TQ71

Netherfield Place
Tel (04246) 4455

This elegant Georgian-style country house hotel stands in 30 acres of beautiful parkland, and is a real haven for those seeking a relaxed and tranquil afternoon tea in luxurious rural surroundings. Tea can be taken in the elegantly furnished lounge in front of a log fire when the weather is chilly, or in the garden if it is fine. Netherfield offers a choice of tea blends, all served with individuality and traditional style. The professional patisserie includes Madeira cake, homemade shortbread and freshly-baked scones. The hotel has its own walled kitchen garden, and in season guests can enjoy fresh berries with cream. The afternoon tea menu provides excellent value for money.

Set afternoon tea £4.50
Open all year, every day, 3 – 5.30pm (for afternoon tea)
Meals available

1   2   3

BATTLE   East Sussex   Map 05 TQ71

The Pilgrims Rest
Tel (04246) 2314

Located next to the abbey in Battle, this early 14th-century building is full of old-world charm. The original beams are exposed, and there are leaded-light windows and wood-burning open fires when the weather is cold. Sussex cream teas are served throughout the afternoon, and tempting offerings include pastries and cakes, fruit scones, hot toast and ice cream surprises.

Set afternoon tea £2.50
Open Apr – Mar, every day, 10am – 5.30pm (limited opening during winter)
Morning coffee and lunches available

BEACONSFIELD   Buckinghamshire   Map 04 SU99

Georgian Coffee House
Wycombe End
Beaconsfield Old Town
Tel (0444) 67855

The Georgian Coffee House is set in an old two-storey building in the centre of the old town. The rooms are well-decorated and inviting, with carpeted floors. A good pot of tea is served by pleasant and attentive staff, and there are homemade cakes, scones and shortbread.

Average price of afternoon tea £2.50
Open all year, Mon – Sat, 9am – 5.30pm

BEAUMARIS   Gwynedd   Map 06 SH67

Spinning Wheel Tea Rooms
1 Bulkeley Place
Castle Street
Tel (0248) 810338

Situated next to the castle in the main street, this is a bright and inviting tea room. There is an attractive glass case with a wonderful display of homemade cakes, pies and shortbreads, including nutty flapjacks, apple and banana slice and currant slice (our inspector particularly enjoyed the apricot-nut slice). The service is quick and friendly. Boxes of fudge are on sale.

Set cream tea £2.50
Open all year (but may close occasionally in winter), every day, 10am – 5pm
Range of meals and snacks served all day

BEAUMARIS   Gwynedd   Map 06 SH67

**The Welsh Dresser
Tea Shop**
30 Castle Street
Tel (0248) 810851

This small shop, with its low ceiling and exposed beams, dates back to the 15th century. Blue carpets are complemented by pretty blue and white tablecloths, and there is a nice cosy, friendly atmosphere. There is a tempting range of homemade cakes, scones and slices, and a choice of tea blends is available. A very good prospect for an enjoyable afternoon tea. Smoking is not permitted.

Pot of tea 40p
Open all year, every day,
10am – 7pm
Light meals and snacks
available

BEDALE   North Yorkshire   Map 08 SE28

Plummers
North End
Tel (0677) 23432

This old stone-built building is full of character. There are low ceilings and exposed beams; a fire burning in the old-fashioned grate, dark polished tables and matching wheel-back chairs complete the picture of the traditional tearoom. Assorted sandwiches, homemade pastries, scones and cakes are available, accompanied by a good, strong pot of tea (and jug of hot water).

Cream tea £2.50
Open all year, Mon – Sat,
10am – 5pm
Morning coffee and
lunches available

BEDDGELERT   Gwynedd   Map 06 SH54

**Beddgelert Tea
Rooms**
Waterloo House
Tel (0766) 86543

Situated by the river bridge in the centre of the village, these tearooms are part of an antique shop. This is a delightful little place, with antique tables and a lovely old stone-built fireplace. A tempting array of cakes and bara brith is available – all homemade. A choice of good flavour tea comes in brown crockery pots, with bone china cups and saucers.

Pot of tea 40p – 45p, cakes
from 50p
Open mid Mar – mid Jan,
every day, 10am – 6pm
(7pm in summer)
Light lunches and snacks
available

BEDFORD   Bedfordshire   Map 04 TL04

Bedford Swan
The Embankment
Tel (0234) 46565

Set on the riverside at Bedford, this 18th-century hotel has upgraded its public rooms to provide comfortable lounge accommodation where afternoon teas are served. Scones, cakes, gâteaux and sandwiches are available, and the service is efficient and friendly. A choice of tea blends is offered.

Set afternoon tea £3
Open all year, every day, 3
– 5.30pm (for afternoon
tea)
Meals available
1 2 3

BERWICK-UPON-TWEED   Northumberland   Map 12 NT95

King's Arms Hotel
(Garden Terrace
Restaurant)
Hide Hill
Tel (0289) 307454

This is a spacious, tastefully decorated self-service restaurant, part of an impressive, stone-built hotel. In fine weather tea can be taken on the patio of the sheltered walled garden. The choice for tea includes shortbread, scones, gâteaux, cheesecakes, malt loaf, pastries and sandwiches. A choice of tea blends is available.

Pot of tea 35p
Open all year, every day,
9.30am – 5.30pm
(occasionally closed Sat
afternoons)
1 2 3

BETWS-Y-COED   Gwynedd   Map 06 SH75

Alpine Coffee Shop
The Railway Station
Tel (06902) 747

This small, bright and fresh coffee shop – decorated in yellow and green – is situated overlooking the railway platform. A good range of snacks is available from the self-service counter, and there is a veranda on the platform if the weather is fine. The tea has a good flavour and the welcome is friendly.

Tea approx 45p
Open all year (except for one month in winter), every day, 9am – 5pm

BEVERLEY   Humberside   Map 08 TA03

Beverley Arms
North Bar Within
Tel (0482) 869241

This modernised country inn is set in the centre of this attractive market town. Tea is served in the rambling lounge areas. The patio lounge and the old kitchen lounge both have original flagged floors; one overlooks the garden area, the other features the old range recesses. Gâteaux, scones, cheesecakes and pastries are available, and there is a choice of tea blends.

Set afternoon tea £3.75
Open all year, every day, 9.30am – 7pm
Meals available
1 2 3

BEVERLEY   Humberside   Map 08 TA03

Tickton Grange Hotel
Tickton
Tel (0964) 543666

About a mile from Beverley, this Georgian country house hotel is set in three and a half acres of gardens. Tea is served in the library, and is ideal for an informal, comfortable and peaceful afternoon tea. There are homemade scones, shortbread, meringues and preserves, and good-quality strong tea is served by the courteous and efficient staff.

Cream tea £2.50
Open all year, every day, 10am – 5.30pm
Meals are served
1 2 3

BEWDLEY   Hereford and Worcester   Map 07 SO77

Brunel Craft Centre Tea Room
Westbourne Street
Wribbenhall

An old Victorian School has been converted into an active craft centre – the cosy attractive tearoom is on the ground floor, and there is extra seating outside in the old playground when it is fine. A strong brew tea is provided, and tempting items include homemade lemon meringue, cheesecakes, sponge cake, teacakes and scones. This is very convenient for the Severn Valley Railway.

Cream tea 75p
Open all year, every day, 10am – 5pm

BEWDLEY   Hereford and Worcester   Map 07 SO77

George Hotel
Load Street
Tel (0299) 402117

Afternoon tea at the George Hotel makes a pleasant conclusion to a day out in this charming little town. Served in the comfortable buttery near the foyer, there are fresh scones and an array of pastries from which to choose. Different types of tea include Rwanda, Darjeeling, Earl Grey and Lapsang Souchong.

Pot of tea 50p. Scones and jam 70p
Open every day, 2.30 – 6pm
Light refreshments also served in the morning

BIBURY   Gloucestershire   Map 04 SP10

Jenny Wren
11 The Street
Tel (028574) 555

In a 250-year-old building, this small old-fashioned teashop is just outside the charming village on the A433. In a heavily beamed room with a Cotswold stone fireplace, a pine dresser has a tempting array of homemade cakes, biscuits and gâteaux, with additional items available from the menu. Hot lardy cakes and Cornish clotted cream teas always prove popular. There is a choice of tea blends.

Pot of tea from 45p, cream tea £1.95
Open all year, every day, 11am – 5pm

BIBURY   Gloucestershire   Map 04 SP10

The Swan Hotel
Tel (028574) 204

Lying deep in the Cotswolds on the banks of the River Coln, this former coaching inn is full of character. Tea can be taken in one of the two charming and comfortable lounges, or in the lovely garden in fine weather. The usual cakes and scones are available, as well as a choice of tea blends served in attractive good-quality china.

Cream tea £2.75
Open all year, every day, 2.30 – 5.30pm (for afternoon tea)
Meals are available

BILLESLEY   Warwickshire   Map 04 SP15

Billesley Manor
Alcester
Tel (0789) 400888

This lovely Elizabethan manor house has been converted into an impressive top-class hotel. Teas are served in the comfortable lounge, the attractive panelled bar, or – weather permitting – outside looking into the extensive lawns and magnificent topiary garden. Scones, biscuits and cakes are all baked on the premises, and a choice of tea blends is available.

'Manor House Tea' £5.50
Open all year, every day, 3 – 6pm (for afternoon tea)
Meals served

BISHOP'S CLEEVE   Gloucestershire   Map 03 SO92

North's Village Bakery
Church Road
Tel (024267) 2658

The teashop here is on one side of the bakery – quite a pretty little area, bright and pink with white china. The temptation will be to eat too much; the smell from the bakery – bread, sugars, cakes – is irresistible. There is a small selection of good-flavour teas, and a wide choice of cakes and pastries.

Pot of tea 45p, scone with jam and cream 58p
Open all year, Mon – Sat, 10am – 5pm
Hot snacks and light meals available

BISHOP'S CLEEVE   Gloucestershire   Map 03 SO92

Tarlings Coffee Shop
Tarlings Yard
Church Road
Tel (024267) 6500

A popular meeting place, Tarlings is a bow-fronted shop situated in a small cul-de-sac off the High Street. The café is carpeted, with sturdy tables and chairs, and attractively adorned with oil paintings by the proprietor. There is a choice of Indian or Earl Grey tea, and the cakes are homemade.

Cream tea £1.35
Open all year, Mon – Sat, 9am – 5pm
Light lunches (homemade quiches and soup)

BLACKPOOL   Lancashire   Map 07 SD33

Pembroke Hotel
North Promenade
Tel (0253) 23434

Tea is served in the impressive and very comfortable first-floor lounge of the Pembroke, with a choice of sofas and armchairs with low tables, or dining tables and chairs. Scones, pastries and cakes are baked on the premises, and there is a choice of Indian, Earl Grey or Assam tea. The tea is served in china service by friendly and efficient staff.

Full afternoon tea £3.65
Open all year, every day,
2.30 – 5pm (for afternoon tea)
Meals available
⬜1 ⬜2 ⬜3 ⬜&

BLAKENEY   Gloucestershire   Map 03 SO60

Brook House
Bridge Street
Tel (0594) 517101

In the centre of the village at the bridge, this 300-year-old stone-built cottage has had many uses – it was the village shop for years. The present proprietors, June and Tony Pegg, have now created this restaurant/tearoom which is a real asset to the area. Tony is a furniture restorer and his handiwork is obvious throughout. June is an accomplished cook – as seen in her scones, lemon cake and fruit cake, and a recipe sent from New Zealand by one satisfied customer for curry cake is now an established favourite. A choice of tea blends is available.

Set cream tea £1.50
Open all year, Tue – Sun,
10am – 6pm (5pm in winter)
Lunch and dinner served (and two splendid bedrooms if you eat too much!)
⬜1 ⬜3

BLAKENEY   Norfolk   Map 09 TG04

The Moorings
3 High Street
Tel (0263) 740054

This small but extremely busy café/bistro is just up the street from the quayside. There are steps up to the entrance leading inside to a mouthwatering array of homemade cakes and pastries, and early in the morning a lovely smell of baked bread. Tasty, yet refreshing tea is served by friendly local waitresses throughout the day. There is a wide choice of tea blends.

Pot of tea 55p, Norfolk cream tea £2.60
Open all year, every day (except Dec – Feb closed Tue – Wed), 10am – 7.30pm (5pm in winter)

BOOT   Cumbria   Map 07 NY10

Brook House
Tel (09403) 288

Set in a tiny village in Eskdale, this small family-run hotel offers a good cup of tea and tasty home baking to tourists and fell walkers. Items available include Bakewell tart, shortbread, fruitcake, gingerbread, crunch slice and mincemeat tart.

Pot of tea 50p – 55p
Open all year, every day,
8.30am – 8.30pm

BONTDDU   Gwynedd   Map 06 SH61

Bontddu Hall
Tel (034149) 661

Bontddu Hall is a lovely stone-built Victorian country mansion offering unrivalled views over the Mawddach estuary and the mountains beyond. Tea is served in the elegant Green Room, or on the delightful terraces on fine summer days. A variety of homemade gâteaux and scones is made on the premises, and a choice of tea blends is available. Staff are friendly and very efficient.

Tea £1
Open Mar – Dec, every day, 2 – 5pm (for afternoon tea)
Meals available

BOSHAM   West Sussex   Map 04 SU80

Drifters
Berkley Cottage
Tel (0243) 573517
(evenings)

Drifters is a small contemporary tearoom featuring homemade cakes and a choice of good, fresh-flavoured tea blends. The plain panelled decor is complemented by pretty lace tablecloths and fresh flowers, and the charming picturesque village setting – well known for its antiques and local crafts. Friendly, personal service is offered by the proprietor, Jane Taverner.

Pot of tea 50p, cakes from 35p
Open Easter – Sep, Tue – Sun and bank holiday Mon, 10.30am – 6pm
Morning coffee and light lunches

BOURNEMOUTH   Dorset   Map 04 SZ09

Cumberland Hotel
East Overcliff Drive
Tel (0202) 290722

This large seafront hotel has a particularly well-appointed and spacious lounge, where winged armchairs and deep settees offer comfortable surroundings for tea. A resident pastry chef ensures that there is never any shortage of cakes, and offers a 'gâteaux of the day'. If the weather is fine, tea can be taken on the terrace around the pool.

Pot of tea 75p, high tea £3.95
Open all year, every day, 2.30 – 5.30pm (for afternoon tea)
Meals available

BOURNEMOUTH   Dorset   Map 04 SZ09

Flossie's Restaurant and Take-away
73 Seamoor Road
Westbourne
Tel (0202) 764459

Located among the busy shops of Westbourne, Flossie's is a simply-furnished, cosy place, with red-plush benches, and newspapers to read. A long counter displays a wonderful array of homemade cakes (lunchtime vegetarian dishes are also very good). Selections from the counter are taken to tables by the friendly and helpful staff.

Pot of tea 55p, cakes from 50p
Open all year, Mon – Sat (closed bank holidays), 8am – 5pm (later in summer)
Light lunches

BRANDON   Suffolk   Map 05 TL78

Bridge House Tea Rooms
Bridge House
Tel (0842) 813137

At the back of an antique pine shop, this tearoom is an attractive conservatory area overlooking the Little Ouse. Fresh flowers, a greetings card and a menu are on each antique pine table – a most hospitable and informal prospect for tea. The cakes and scones are homemade, and a good strong pot of tea is served (Earl Grey available).

Pot of tea 50p, scone with jam and cream 75p
Open all year, Thu – Tue, 10am – 6pm
Light lunches
1 3

BRANDON   Suffolk   Map 05 TL78

Copper Kettle
31 High Street
Tel (0842) 814185

Fresh flowers, lace tablecloths, and a warm welcome await prospective visitors to this small high street teashop. A choice of tea blends is available, and cakes include scones, fruit cakes, tea cakes, apple pies and gâteaux – all home-baked. Smoking is not permitted.

Pot of tea for two 80p, set tea £1.95
Open all year, every day (except Mon, but open bank holidays), 9am – 6pm

BRECON   Powys   Map 03 SO02

Brown Sugar Restaurant
12 The Bulwark
Tel (0874) 5501

A beamed ceiling and pine tables and farmhouse chairs contribute to the atmosphere of this small restaurant. The tea has a good flavour (choice of blends) and a display of cakes offers scones, pastries and tarts. A board of local information brochures is a useful bonus for visitors to the area.

Pot of tea 40p
Open all year, every day, 10am – 9.30pm (winter 5pm)
Lunches available

BRECON   Powys   Map 03 SO02

Crusty's Coffee Shop
Country Life and Welsh Flair
High Street
Tel (0874) 2664

Part of a town-centre craft shop, Crusty's is a pine-furnished restaurant – clean and well maintained – with a friendly welcome. There is a very wide selection of pastries, cakes and pies, and bread and cakes are also for sale at the counter. A good pot of tea is served.

Pot of tea 30p
Open all year, Mon – Sat, 8.30am – 5.30pm (Jul – Aug until 6pm)

BRIDGNORTH   Shropshire   Map 07 SO79

George and Bertie's Coffee House
42 High Street
Tel (0746) 761816

This coffee shop (at the back of a bread and cake shop) is in Bridgnorth's busy high street, within walking distance of the Severn Valley Railway. The cakes are all baked at the proprietor's own bakery in Cannock and delivered fresh every day.

Pot of tea 50p
Open all year, Mon – Sat, 9am – 5.30pm (Mon – Fri), 8.45am – 5.15pm (Sat)
Hot snack meals

BRIDPORT   Dorset   Map 03 SY49

Toby Jug
41 South Street
Tel (0308) 25774

This small, cosy, cottage-style tearoom has much character – bay window, exposed beams, wooden tables and chairs. The friendly proprietress serves a good Earl Grey (tea leaves – strainer provided), and a nice selection of scones, cakes and pastries.

Cream tea £1.55
Open all year, Tue – Sat (closed Thu afternoons), 10am – 5pm

BRIGHTON   East Sussex   Map 04 TQ30

The Royal Pavilion
Tel (0273) 603005

The tour of the royal apartments at Brighton Pavilion (£2.30 admission charge) leads to a first-floor self-service cafeteria. Cakes and scones are supplied by local bakeries, and a selection of tea blends is offered. Staff are polite and helpful.

Set tea £1.10
Open all year, every day,
Oct – May 11am – 4.30pm,
Jun – Sep 10.30am – 5pm
Lunches and snacks
available

BROCKENHURST   Hants   Map 04 SU20

The Cottage Hotel
Swan Road
Tel (0590) 22296

True to its name, this is a 16th-century cottage with low doors and ceilings and exposed oak beams – at the rear is a well-kept rockery and lawn with a tea garden terrace. Homemade scones highlight the set cream tea, and China and herb teas are available on request. This is a really attractive setting for a leisurely afternoon tea.

Cream tea £1.95
Open all year, every day, 3
– 6pm (for afternoon tea)
[1] [3]

BROCKENHURST   Hants   Map 04 SU20

**Rhinefield House
Hotel**
Rhinefield Road
Tel (0590) 22922

Built on the site of an old hunting lodge, this Victorian folly is set in 40 acres of grounds, where fallow deer can occasionally be seen grazing. Scones and a selection of gâteaux is available, and a choice of tea blends is served.

Set tea £3.45
Open all year, every day,
3.30 – 5.30pm (for
afternoon tea)
[1] [2] [3]

BROCKENHURST   Hants   Map 04 SU20

**Thatched Cottage
Restaurant**
16 Brookley Road
Tel (0590) 23090

This restaurant is an absolute winner for afternoon tea. Inside this gem of a thatched cottage there are four interconnecting rooms in which to have tea – two with open fires. The menu is mouthwatering, with offerings of scones and clotted cream, finger sandwiches and a selection of cheesecakes – homemade and served warm – including lemon, apple, chocolate, and strawberry. There are also cakes (plain, fruited, wholemeal with walnuts), and a selection of tea blends (Indian, China and English breakfast) and herbal infusions. Several flavours of New Forest ice cream are also available. But one thing really did excite our inspector: '... joy of joys: tea cosies!! A real find.'

'Complete Cream Tea' £3
Open all year, Wed – Mon,
2.30 – 6.30pm (for
afternoon tea)

BROUGHTON   Borders   *Lanarkshire*   Map 11 NT13

The Thirty Nine Steps Tel (08994) 279	Situated on the A701 on the northern approach to the village, this attractive little gift shop and tearoom was once the village school. Scones, cakes and toasted teacakes are available – all homemade, and there is a choice of Ceylon, Earl Grey, mint or lemon tea. The service is pleasant and efficient. Smoking is not permitted.	Pot of tea from 35p, cakes from 40p Open Easter – Oct, Sun – Mon 2 – 5pm, Tue – Sat 10.30am – 5pm Set lunch available (including homemade soup)

BURFORD   Oxfordshire   Map 04 SP21

Andrews Hotel and Coffee House High Street Tel (099382) 3151	This stylish character Cotswold hotel in Burford's attractive high street offers excellent standards of home baking in very comfortable surroundings. Good service is provided by the pleasant staff. A choice of tea blends is available. Smoking is not permitted.	Pot of tea £1.30, set tea £3.25 Open all year, every day, 10.30am – 5pm 1 2 3

BURFORD   Oxfordshire   Map 04 SP21

Huffkins High Street Tel (099382) 2126	This teashop/restaurant is on the first floor – above a bakery shop – and panelled floors, whitewashed walls and wheel-back chairs give an intimate cottage atmosphere. Homemade scones, pastries, croissants and rich tea cakes are available, and a choice of tea blends is served in nice china. No smoking is permitted.	Pot of tea 55p, cream tea £1.95 Open Apr – Nov, every day, 10am – 5pm

BURLEY   Hampshire   Map 04 SU20

Manor Farm Tea Rooms Ringwood Road Tel (04253) 2218	A 16th-century cottage houses these well-known tearooms, with exposed beams and original inglenook fireplace. Friendly and obliging staff serve good cakes (including a Shrewsbury biscuit gâteau). There is a good choice of China, Indian, Celon and English breakfast teas.	Cottage tea £1.50, high tea £3.90 Open all year, every day (except Mon morning), 10am – 5.30pm (5pm in winter)

BURLEY   Hampshire   Map 04 SU20

**Old Station
Tearooms**
Holmsley
Tel (04253) 2468

Just off the A35 Lyndhurst – Bournemouth road, this
old railway station has been nicely converted into an
extensive tearoom with a large tea garden. The
gardens are particularly neat and well-maintained.
Scones, flapjacks, shortbread, chocolate gâteaux are
available, and efficient aproned ladies serve tea
(China or lemon available).

Cream tea £1.80
Open all year, every day
Mar – Dec, Sat – Sun only
Jan – Feb, 10am – 5.30pm
Lunches served

BURY ST EDMUNDS   Suffolk   Map 05 TL86

Angel Hotel
Angel Hill
Tel (0284) 753926

Afternoon tea at the Angel is served by efficient
uniformed staff in the very comfortable and tastefully
decorated hotel lounge. A choice of good-flavoured
teas are available, served in bone china. The set tea
includes scones with fresh cream and jam, home-
baked cakes and scones and hot buttered toast.

Pot of tea £1.50, full
afternoon tea £4.50
Open 3.30 – 5.30pm (for
tea)
Meals available
1   2   3

BURY ST EDMUNDS   Suffolk   Map 05 TL86

Porters
5 Whiting Street
Tel (0284) 706198

This light and airy teashop is nicely furnished – prints
on the walls, pot plants, wicker chairs and pretty floral
tablecloths. Uniformed staff serve scones, croissants,
tea bread, gâteaux, homemade cakes, cinnamon toast
and sandwiches. There is a choice of good flavoured
tea blends.

Pot of tea 60p, cream tea
£2
Open all year, every day,
9.30am – 5.30pm (except
Sun, 12 noon – 3pm)
&

CALDBECK   Cumbria   Map 11 NY33

**Water Mill Coffee
Shop**
Priests Mill
Tel (06998) 369

This delightful riverside setting is an ideal spot for a
tranquil afternoon tea. The mill was restored in 1985,
and now houses craft shops, workshops and
exhibition areas as well as this attractive, well-ordered
cafe. The friendly helpful staff serve excellent home-
baked cakes, scones and tea breads, and choice of tea
blends.

Pot of tea 50p
Open mid Mar – Oct, Tue
– Sun and bank holiday
Mon; Nov – Dec Sat – Sun
only, 10.30am – 5pm
Full meals and light
refreshments served all
day

CAERNARFON   Gwynedd   Map 06 SH46

Rochelle's
25 Bridge Street
Tel (0286) 5110

A well furnished coffee shop and restaurant situated
in the town centre. There is an interesting display of
pot plants, mirrors and old pictures, and a 1950s juke
box plays old rock and roll records. A range of
gâteaux, cheesecakes and scones is served from
attractive pink and white crockery. There is a choice
of three loose tea blends.

Open Jan – Dec, Mon –
Sat, 9am – 6pm (9am –
9pm Fri – Sat)
Meals served all day

CALLANDER Central *Perthshire* Map 11 NN60

Pips Coffee House and Gallery
21–23 Ancaster Square
Tel (0877) 30470

A smart little coffee shop tucked in a corner of the square just off the main street. White furniture creates a bright, airy atmosphere, while walls are heavily adorned with framed pictures. A tasty range of salads and freshly cut sandwiches is offered, with a choice of tea blends. Sweet temptations include cheesecakes and fruit pies served with cream, scones and delicious homemade shortbread.

Pot of tea 45 – 50p
Open Jan – Dec, Easter – Oct 10am – 8pm every day, Nov – Easter 10am – 5pm closed Wed
Lunch, evening menu available in summer
[1] [3]

CAMBRIDGE Cambridgeshire Map 05 TL45

Henry's Teashop
5A Pembroke Street
Tel (0223) 61206

Part of a shop selling teas, coffees and unusual tea-pots, this is a small tearoom with wood panels, some stained glass, prints and plants. There are wheelback chairs and round tables clothed in white crochet lace, set with vases of dried flowers. Homemade cakes, pastries and a choice of tea blends are served from floral crockery. Smoking is not permitted.

Tea 60p
Open Jan – Dec, Mon – Sat, 9am – 5.15pm

CAMBRIDGE Cambridgeshire Map 05 TL45

Fitzbillies
52 Trumpington Street
Tel (0223) 352500

A small tearoom over a cake shop, the décor is simple: a pine fireplace, prints, clothed tables and fresh flowers. The menu is hand written, offering sandwiches, homebaked scones, cakes, pastries and a choice of Indian, China and fruit teas.

Tea 50p, set afternoon tea £2.75
Open Jan – Dec, Tue – Sun (Mon pm only), 8.30am – 5.30pm

CARDIFF South Glamorgan Map 03 ST17

Celtic Cauldron
47–49 Castle Arcade
Tel (0222) 387185

Directly opposite the castle, this tearoom is furnished with farmhouse-style chairs and tables set on bare floorboards. Mostly wholefood baking, snacks and vegetarian meals are offered, with a choice of tea blends, including herbal, served from earthenware pottery.

Tea 40p
Open Jan – Dec, Mon – Sat, 11am – 6pm
Snacks and vegetarian meals available
[1] [2] [3]

CARDIFF South Glamorgan Map 03 ST17

Chattery Coffee Shop
Excalibur Drive,
Thornhill
Tel (0222) 766667

Modern self-service coffee shop in mini shopping centre with waitress assistance for hot meals. Sandwiches, snacks, scones and pastries are offered with a choice of Indian and China teas.

Tea £1
Open Jan – Dec, Mon – Sat, 9am – 6pm Mon – Wed, 9am – 7pm Thu – Sat
Snacks and hot meals available

CARLISLE   Cumbria   Map 12 NY45

Bullough's
Castle Street
Tel (0228) 24202

This stylish, well-run cafeteria is part of Bullough's department store, opposite the Cathedral. There is a salad bar and hot and cold meals are available on a self-service basis. Tea is served in stainless steel pots and a choice of blends is offered. There is a good range of homemade scones, cakes and pastries.

Pot of tea 38p – 40p
Open Jan – Dec, Mon –
Sat, 9am – 5.30pm
Lunches available
1 2 3

CARLISLE   Cumbria   Map 12 NY45

**The Grapevine
Restaurant**
22 Fisher Street
Tel (0228) 46617

Housed in part of the YMCA building, this spacious, bistro-style restaurant is lively, friendly and full of character, and specialities include wholefoods and a wide range of salads as well as teas. The Grapevine offers a choice of teas and herbal infusions, with a wide selection of homemade scones, tea breads, cakes and puddings.

Pot of speciality tea 50p
Open all year, Mon – Sat,
9.30am – 4.30pm

CARLISLE   Cumbria   Map 12 NY45

**Hudsons Coffee
Shop**
17 Fisher Street
Tel (0228) 47733

Situated in the old City Council's Treasurer's building, this small, busy coffee shop specialises in snacks, cakes and biscuits made on the premises using only natural ingredients and avoiding the use of preservatives, colouring and excess salt. A variety of teas and coffees is available; tea is loose leaf, served in a stainless steel pot with strainer. Smoking is not permitted.

Pot of tea 55p, cream tea
£2.15
Open Jan – Dec, Mon –
Sat, 9.30am – 5pm
Snacks available

CARLISLE   Cumbria   Map 12 NY45

**Watt's Victorian
Coffee Shop**
11 Bank Street
Tel (0228) 21545

A busy coffee shop with a friendly atmosphere and the delicious aroma of roasting beans. A good range of tea blends is available and well-flavoured leaf tea is served in a traditional pot with strainer, on converted sewing machine tables. There is a wide selection of homemade cakes, scones and biscuits. High class groceries are also stocked.

Pot of tea 55p, set
afternoon tea £2.20
Open Jan – Dec, Mon –
Sat, 9.30am – 5pm
Light lunches available

CARMARTHEN   Dyfed   Map 02 SN42

**Old Curiosity
Restaurant**
20A King Street
Tel (0267) 232384

Situated in the centre of Carmarthen, close to the castle, this restaurant offers a good selection of cream cakes, gâteaux and scones, as well as full meals and light snacks. One may choose from a variety of tea blends.

Open Jan – Dec, Mon –
Sat, 9am – 6pm Mon –
Tue, 9am – midnight Wed
– Sat
Lunch and dinner

1 3

CARMARTHEN Dyfed Map 02 SN42

Tuck In
54 King Street
Tel (0267) 233157

Long narrow cafe with plastic furniture. Cheerful staff serve a range of scones, welsh cakes, cream cakes and fruit pies, as well as a large selection of hot meals. Tea is available by the mug only in the busy period from noon to three o'clock. At other times it can be served by the pot.

Tea and cake 70p
Open Jan – Dec, Mon – Sat, 7.30am – 5pm
Snacks and hot meals

CARRBRIDGE Tayside *Inverness-shire* Map 14 NH92

The Ecclefechan
Tel (047984) 374

A bright modern bistro, patisserie and coffee house set back from the main road in the centre of the village. A choice of teas is offered, and a selection of homemade scones, cakes, pastries and pancakes.

Pot of tea 50p
Open Jan – Dec, Wed – Mon, 10am – 10pm
Lunch and dinner

CARRBRIDGE Tayside *Inverness-shire* Map 14 NH92

Landmark Highland Heritage & Adventure Park
Tel (047984) 614

Large self-service restaurant within the Highland Heritage and Adventure Park (to which an admission fee is payable). The restaurant offers a wide range of scones, cakes and fruit tarts. Tea is served in stainless steel teapots with sachets of sugar and individual UHT milk cartons. There is a salad bar and hot meals are also available.

Open Jan – Dec, Mon – Sat, 9.30am – 5.30pm
(9.30am – 4pm Nov – Mar)
Lunch

CARTMEL Cumbria Map 07 SD37

The Priory Hotel
The Square
Tel (05395) 36267

The Prior's Refectory adjoins the main hotel, where bow windows and lace-covered tables adorn this attractive tearoom. Tea is freshly made and there is a choice of Indian or Earl Grey. Homemade scones, cakes and gâteaux are available, and the staff are friendly and efficient.

Pot of tea 55p, cream tea £1.65
Open all year, Tue – Sun and bank holiday Mon, 10.30am – 5pm

CARTMEL Cumbria Map 07 SD37

St Mary's Lodge
Tel (05395) 36379

The front room of this inviting period guest house provides a homely setting for afternoon tea. Genuinely homemade and good cakes and scones accompany China or Earl Grey teas.

Pot of tea 55p, set afternoon tea £2.50
Open Apr – mid Nov, every day, 2.30 – 5.30pm

CASTLE HEADINGHAM   Essex   Map 05 TL84

Colne Valley Railway Restaurant
Yeldham Road
Tel (0787) 61174

Part of the privately-run Colne Valley Railway, this unusual teashop is a converted 1950s restaurant car, retaining its original seats and tables. There is a good choice of tea, with tempting delicacies such as cinnamon toast, flapjack, scones, sponge cakes and gâteaux, to go with it. The staff are very friendly and welcoming.

Cream tea £2.25
Open every day except Jan and in difficult weather conditions 10am – 5pm

---

CERNE ABBAS   Dorset   Map 02 SY79

Old Market House
25 Long Street
Tel (03003) 680

A Georgian building with large double window front. The décor is simple but pleasant, tables are clothed and well spaced and the crockery is bone china. Tea is served in stainless steel pots. Homemade scones, cakes, sponges and sandwiches are available and lunch is also served. Smoking is not permitted.

Cream tea £1.75
Open Mar – Oct, every day, 10am – 5pm
Lunch

CERNE ABBAS   Dorset   Map 02 SY79

The Singing Kettle
7 Long Street
Tel (03003) 3349

This is a small ground floor room in a large, double fronted Georgian house in the village centre, pleasantly decorated with a number of pictures and ornaments and an assortment of wooden tables. A choice of teas is available, and a selection of scones, cakes and shortbread. Tea is served from a stainless steel pot with china crockery. Smoking is not permitted.

Cream tea £1.80
Open Easter – Sep, Tue – Sun, 10.30am – 5.30pm
Lunch

CHARMOUTH   Dorset   Map 03 SY39

White House Hotel
2 Hillside, The Street
Tel (0297) 60411

A small hotel in the centre of the town with a well appointed lounge, attractive garden and patio. A choice of tea blends and a selection of scones and cakes are served.

Tea £1.75
Open Jan – Dec, every day, 3pm – 5pm
1 3

CHARNOCK RICHARD   Lancashire   Map 07 SD52

Emily's
Park Hall Hotel
Tel (0257) 452090

According to the poem inside the menu, this delightful tearoom is named after the lady who recognised that 'Afternoon Tea is better than lunch!', and set about making the Chorley Bun her speciality. Situated in the attractive square at the heart of the hotel, there is an old world charm reflecting a more genteel era which makes this an inviting place to sample other traditional delicacies such as Goosnagh cakes, Dinkie pikelets and Eccles cakes. All the cakes and pastries are baked locally to the recipes used by Emily's grandmother, and complemented by a range of speciality teas which includes Emily's Special Tea Room Blend.

Pot of tea £1.15, tea and cream cake £2.75
Open all year, every day, 10 – 5pm (10 – 6pm weekends)

1 2 3 &

CHAWTON   Hampshire   Map 04 SU73

Cassandra's Cup
Tel (0420) 83144

Opposite Jane Austen's house in the pretty village of Chawton, Cassandra's Cup is a pleasant place to take tea. A selection of speciality teas is available, and delicious homemade cakes which might include chocolate, orange, coffee, lemon or fruitcake. Service is prompt and courteous.

Pot of tea 45p – 50p, cake 70p
Open Dec – Oct (closed part Nov), every day, 10.30am – 5pm

CHELMSFORD   Essex   Map 05 TL70

Pontlands Park Hotel
West Hanningfield Road, Great Baddow
Tel (0245) 76444

A tastefully modernised country house hotel where tea is served in the comfortably appointed lounge. Salmon and cucumber sandwiches, scones with butter, jam and cream, and continental-style pastries are available. A choice of teas is offered, served in the traditional way by friendly staff.

Cream tea £3, set tea £5
Open Jan – Dec, Mon – Sun, 3pm – 6pm

1 2 3

CHESTER   Cheshire   Map 07 SJ46

The Chester Grosvenor
Eastgate Street
Tel (0244) 324024

Whether in the magnificent La Brasserie or the elegant Library lounge, with its quiet sophistication, afternoon tea will be a civilised and memorable occasion at this excellent city centre hotel. The leaf tea is served in delightful silverware and there is a wide range of tempting cakes and pastries.

Afternoon tea £7.50
Open all year except Christmas Day and Boxing Day, every day, 3 – 5pm
Light lunches and morning coffee

CHESTER   Cheshire   Map 07 SJ46

Chester Visitor Centre
Vicars Lane
Tel (0244) 351609

Styled in the manner of a Tudor courtyard, this cafeteria and restaurant is part of an impressive visitor and tourist centre. There is a limited selection of scones, cakes and pastries with a choice of tea blends. Tea is currently served in plastic pots, but these are to be replaced with stainless steel. Sandwiches and hot meals are also available.

Tea 45p – £1.10, set tea £1.85
Open Jan – Dec, every day, 9am – 9pm

CHESTER   Cheshire   Map 07 SJ46

Next Coffee Shop
37 Eastgate Street
Tel (0244) 329591

A smart in-store coffee shop in Chester's fashionable Eastgate Street. Self-service, with helpful counter staff, various blends of tea are available with some homemade cakes, cream cakes and scones. Light hot dishes, soups, pizza, chilli and excellent salads are also offered.

Pot of tea 50p, cakes 65p – £1.05
Open Jan – Dec, Mon – Sat, 9.30am – 5pm
Light lunches

CHESTER   Cheshire   Map 07 SJ46

The Witches Kitchen
19 Frodsham Street
Tel (0244) 311836

An Elizabethan-style building, allegedly haunted, close to the Cathedral. Friendly staff serve scones, gâteaux and various cakes with a choice of tea blends. But dishes are served at lunch and dinner and pizzas are available all day.

Set tea £1.95
Open Jan – Dec, Mon – Sun, 9am – 6pm (Sun noon – 9.30) tea served 2.30pm – 6pm
Lunch, dinner

CHEWTON MENDIP   Somerset   Map 03 ST65

Chewton Cheese Dairy
Priory Farm
Tel (076 121) 666

Interesting teashop over the Chewton Cheese Dairy. Cheese-making can be viewed from a gallery and the cheddar is on sale, along with other local produce, in the shop next door (closed Sundays). The tearoom is pretty, in pine with bare floorboards. The food display is tempting, and the cakes, scones, soups and pies are all freshly homebaked.

Set tea £1.60
Open mid Feb – mid Jan, every day, 10am – 4pm
Lunch

CHIDEOCK   Dorset   Map 03 SY49

Betchworth Hotel
Tel (0297) 89478

Small cottage guesthouse on the main road. Tea, scones and cakes are served at wooden tables in the low ceilinged, beamed dining room or at tables in the garden. Earl Grey and Jasmine teas are also available.

Cream tea £1.85, tea and cake £1.50
Open Mar – Oct, every day

CHIPPERFIELD   Hertfordshire   Map 04 TL00

The Two Brewers
The Common
Tel (09277) 65266

Dating from the late 17th century this charming hotel, located on the village common, offers a relaxed and pleasant atmosphere. Tea is served in the comfortable lounge with sugar bowl, milk jug and well flavoured tea. A selection of blends is available.

Pot of tea 85p, set tea £3.25
Open Jan – Dec, every day
| 1 | | 2 | | 3 |

CHIPPING CAMPDEN   Gloucestershire   Map 04 SP13

Greenstocks
The Cotswold House
Tel (0386) 840330

Greenstocks is a café-bar attached to this lovely Cotswold town hotel. Food is served all day from breakfast to supper. For afternoon tea, apart from a wide choice of tea blends, there is the traditional cream tea with homemade scones and Jersey cream, buttered pikelets or cinnamon toast and a variety of cakes and pastries.

Set tea £1.95
Open Jan – Dec (except Christmas), everyday, 9.30am – 9.30pm (10pm Sat)
Breakfast, substantial lunch and supper
| 1 | | 2 | | 3 |

CHIPPING NORTON   Oxfordshire   Map 04 SP23

The Old Bakehouse Restaurant and Tearoom
50 West Street
Tel (0608) 3441

Tiny cottage teashop with flagstone floor, rough cast walls and beamed ceiling. There is a fascinating display of pictures, antiques, objets d'art and a fine collection of old teddy bears. Tea is served in traditional style with a selection of blends, Bakehouse pâté, scones, fruitcake and jams. Tables are set with old-fashioned linen and dainty bone china. Smoking is not permitted.

Pot of tea 50p, cream tea £2.50
Open Jan – Dec, every day, 10am – 6pm
| 1 | | 3 |

CHORLEY   Lancashire   Map 07 SD51

Muffins
12 High Street
Tel (02572) 62566

A quaint town centre teashop personally managed by the proprietors. Cakes, pastries and biscuits are baked on the premises and are also sold to take home. Bread and muffins are baked locally. Light lunches and snacks are served fresh from the kitchens and a choice of tea blends is available. Smoking is not permitted.

Set tea £2
Open Jan – Dec, Mon – Sat, 9am – 4.30pm
Light lunches and snacks

CHURCH STRETTON   Shropshire   Map 07 SO49

Mynd House
Little Stretton
Tel (0694) 722212

A small two star hotel in a peaceful location. Tea is generally served in the comfortable lounge. A large choice of tea blends, crumpets, Danish pastries, meringues and scones are offered.

Tea £1 (minimum)
Open Feb – Dec, every day, 2pm – 4.45pm

| 1 | | 3 |

CIRENCESTER   Gloucestershire   Map 04 SP00

Rosamond De Marco
Shop 7
Swan Yard
West Market Street
Tel (0285) 659683

Among an old courtyard of interesting shops, this tearoom also sells handmade Belgian chocolates. Continental pâtisserie is the main feature of the menu in this clean, cosy establishment. Tea is served from pretty porcelain crockery, and a selection of blends is available. Smoking is not permitted.

Pot of tea 50p – 55p, pâtisserie 45p – £1
Open Jan – Dec, every day, 9.30am – 6pm in summer, 10am – 5.30pm in winter
Lunches available

1   3

CLARE   Suffolk   Map 05 TL74

Ship Stores
22 – 23 Callis Street
Tel (0787) 277834

This small character tearoom is part of a village shop, though the entrance is separate. There is a cottage atmosphere with wooden tables, upright chairs, bone china crockery and an assortment of pots. Outside seating is also available. There is a blackboard menu offering sandwiches and snacks, and a selection of homemade cakes is displayed.

Tea 30p, set tea 90p
Open Jan-Dec, every day, 10am – 6pm
Snacks

CLAWTON   Devon   Map 02 SX39

Court Barn Hotel
Tel (040927) 219

Attractive manor house with five acres of gardens amidst rolling countryside. A lovely setting in which to enjoy traditional afternoon tea. Choose from around twenty-five speciality tea blends served with scones and Devon cream, homemade jams, marmalades, cakes and pastries.

Set tea £2.50
Open Feb – Dec, every day, 3pm – 6pm

1   2

COLEFORD   Gloucestershire   Map 03 SO51

Muffins Restaurant
12 St John Street
Tel (0594) 34841

A friendly restaurant in the heart of the lovely Forest of Dean, Muffins is open for various meals from breakfast to high tea. Toasted muffins are the speciality of the house, scones and cakes are all homemade. A variety of blends and herbal teas are available, served in stainless steel pots. The lunch and high tea menus include items suitable for vegetarians.

Pot of tea 45p – 50p
Open Jan – Dec, every day, 8am – 5.30pm   (7pm in school summer holiday), Sun after May noon – 7pm

CONWY Gwynned Map 06 SH77

The Quayway
5 High Street
Tel (0492) 592937

Situated above a row of shops, close to the Castle and Quay, with a friendly, simple style, giving good value for money. A blackboard menu offers light meals, toasted sandwiches, homemade cakes and puddings. Well-flavoured tea is served in stainless steel pots at prettily clothed tables.

Pot of tea 65p
Open Jan – Dec, Mon –
Sat, 9am – 8pm summer,
11am – 5pm winter

CONWY Gwynedd Map 06 SH77

Victorian Teashop
Hallmark Antiques
7 Berry Street
Tel (0492) 592567

A teashop with a truly Welsh flavour in the heart of the town. Here the tables are set among the antique items for sale which makes for a pleasant and conversational environment. Lace clothed tables, Indian Tree crockery and tapped male voice choir music all contribute to the atmosphere. Various snacks and a range of homemade cakes are available with a choice of tea blends.

Pot of tea 60p
Open Jan – Dec, every day,
8am – 10pm
Snacks

CORRIS Powys Map 06 SH71

Teddy Bears' Picnic
Lower Corris
Tel (065 473) 412

The identifying characteristic of this establishment is the collection of teddy bears on display and for sale. For the 'picnic' choose from a range of sweet fare including cookies, hot bread pudding, welshcakes and scones.

Tea 35p
Open from 9th May for
season, Sun 2pm – 6pm,
Tue, Thu and Fri 11am –
6pm

CRAWLEY West Sussex Map 04 TQ24

Tudor Coffee Shop
The George
High Street
Tel (0293) 24215

The George is easily recognised by its gallows sign which spans the High Street. The Tudor Coffee Shop offers a good selection of food, 'Anytimers', Just Sweets' and 'Main Dishes', and children are made particularly welcome. Tea is served throughout the afternoon by uniformed staff from china teapots, milk jugs and sugar bowls, with hot fruit scones and pâtisseries.

Set tea £2.15
Open Jan – Dec, every day,
9am – 9.45pm
Light meals, lunch and
dinner
| 1 | | 2 | | 3 |

CRICCIETH Gwynedd Map 06 SH43

Granvilles Coffee Shop
High Street
Tel (076671) 2168

A bright fresh coffee shop and restaurant on the main road. Black and gold frontage, cream and black décor with a tiled floor, Victorian fireplace, mock marble topped tables and piped music. A good range of meals is served all day, and there is a display of homemade cakes including bara brith and excellent doughnuts and scones.

Tea 50p
Open all year everyday
9.30am – 9.30pm
Meals all day
| 1 | | 3 |

CRINAN   Strathclyde *Argyllshire*   Map 10 NR79

Crinan Coffee Shop Tel (054683) 261	Delightfully situated beside the western basin of the Crinan Canal, the former canal horse stables have been attractively converted. The self-service counter displays a delicious array of baking from the nearby hotel kitchens: doughnuts, cakes and scones, and some savoury items too, such as quiche, sausage rolls and open sandwiches. Homemade ice cream is also popular. Some speciality teas are available.	Pot of tea 55p – 65p Open Easter – Oct, every day, 9am – 5pm

CULLEN   Grampian   *Banffshire*   Map 15 NJ56

The Tea Cozy 8–10 The Square Tel (0542) 40638	Small neatly laid out teashop in a corner site of central Cullen. Simple but pleasant, plates and pictures adorn the walls and there is a display of dried flowers in the window. A small selection of homemade scones, biscuits and cakes is served. A choice of blends is available and tea is served in stainless steel teapots.	Pot of tea 50p Open Jan – Dec, every day 10am – 5pm (6pm in summer)

DALBEATTIE   Dumfries and Galloway   Map 10 NX97

Coffee and Things 32 High Street Tel (0556) 611033	Smartly decorated teashop offering a civilised environment with leaf tea served in china pots and Wedgwood crockery. There is a display of china for sale and a small shop at the rear selling bric-à-brac. Lunches are served between 12 and 2pm and there is a small range of good homemade cakes, scones and biscuits. Indian, Ceylon and China teas are available.	Pot of tea 45p Open mid Mar – Dec, Tue – Sat, 10am – 5pm Lunch

DALBEATTIE   Dumfries and Galloway   Map 10 NX97

The Gift Gallery 14 High Street Tel (0556) 610404	Small neatly laid out tea and coffee shop, serving snacks and a small range of homebaked scones, biscuits and puddings such as lemon meringue pie. Tea is made in a stainless steel pot. Service is friendly and efficient.	Pot of tea 40p Open Jan – Dec, Mon – Sat, 8am – 5pm Snacks

DEDHAM   Essex   Map 05 TM03

The Essex Rose Teahouse Royal Square Tel (0206) 323101	This fine building was once a Master Weaver's house and still retains many of the original beams. Personally directed by the Bower family, it is often busy, but well worth a visit for the delicious home baking, served by the friendly staff. The mouthwatering cakes include lemon torte, chocolate layer cake and toasted teacakes on a cold winter's day.	Pot of tea 60p, cream tea £2.40 Open all year (except Dec 25 – 27), every day, 9am – 6pm

DELAMERE   Cheshire   Map 07 SJ57

Romany Tearoòm
Chester Road
Delamere Forest
Tel (0606) 882032

A charming little tearoom featuring white wrought iron patio furniture and intricate model Romany caravans. Situated in a caravan sales complex together with a large accessory shop alongside the A556 close to Delamere Forest. Mouthwatering homemade cakes, scones and gâteaux are served at the counter, and savouries such as sandwiches, pasties, lasagne and moussaka.

Pot of tea 40p
Open Jan – Dec (except Christmas and New Year), every day, 10am – 5pm

DINAS MAWDDWY   Gwynedd.   Map 06 SH81

The Old Station Coffee Shop
Tel (06504) 261

Situated in the old railway station, with pine tables and chairs, the coffee shop is self-service with a super display of homemade cakes and scones. There are large cakes for sale and take-away picnic food. Light lunches include homemade soups, pizzas, quiche, sandwiches and salads. Several blends of tea, including herbal, are available and are served in stainless steel pots.

Open mid Mar – mid Nov and Dec 27 for 10 days, every day 9.30am – 5pm
Light lunches

DISLEY   Cheshire   Map 07 SJ98

The Village Tearoom
7 Market Street
Tel (0663) 64259

A former spinner's cottage situated on the A6 in the centre of the village. In addition to set teas this tearoom serves morning coffee and lunches, with vegetarian dishes available. All cakes and scones are homemade, and a choice of tea blends is offered.

Cream tea £1.50, Cheshire tea £2.50, full afternoon tea £5 for two
Open Jan – Dec, every day, 10am – 6pm

DODDWOOD UNDER SKIDDAW   Cumbria   Map 11 NY

The Old Sawmill
Tel (07687) 74317

The Old Sawmill was built in 1880 to prepare the larches felled on the Mirehouse estate, and was still in use until 1970. On the walls are tools and pictures from the Mill's past, and the original machinery, still in place, is now a feature of this fascinating tearoom. The Manor house is open to the public and there are many walks through the woods. No smoking is permitted.

Pot of tea 35p, scone with rum butter 55p
Open Easter – Oct 31, every day, 10.30am – 5.30pm
Snack lunches available

DOLGELLAU   Gwynedd   Map 06 SH71

Yr Hen Efail
Tel (0341) 422977

Yr Hen Efail means 'old smithy' and this small café is located in an old smithy by the large public car park near the river. The café is plain and simple, offering a range of meals throughout the day at reasonable prices. Good homemade fruit pies are also served.

Welsh teas £2
Open during season depending on available trade, Mon – Sun, 9am – 11pm
Meals served all day

DOLPHINTON   Strathclyde *Lanarkshire*   Map 11 NT14

**Beechwood
Tearoom**
Tel (0968) 82285

Small roadside tearoom, clean and neat inside with solid fuel stove and pictures displayed available for sale. One can also buy homemade jam and marmalade. Tea is served with a small selection of homemade cakes, biscuits and scones.

Pot of tea 50p, full
afternoon tea £2.25
Open Feb – Dec, every
day, 10am – 6pm

DORCHESTER   Dorset   Map 03 SY69

Potter In
19 Durngate Street
Tel (0305) 68649

Small 17th century house with seating on two floors, pine tables and chairs and a well stocked counter of homemade wholemeal cakes and pastries. Twelve blends of tea, including herbal, are offered. Service is helpful and friendly, vegetarians are catered for and smoking is not permitted.

Cream tea £1.65
Open all year Mon – Sat,
10am – 5pm
Lunch
1 3

DORKING   Surrey   Map 04 TQ14

**Burford Bridge
Hotel**
Boxhill
Tel (0306) 884561

A charming hotel set amidst beautiful gardens on the bank of the River Mole and edging onto Boxhill Country Park. Tea is served in the comfortable lounge with sandwiches, scones, pastries and biscuits. A choice of Indian and China tea blends is available.

Pot of tea £1.75, cream tea
£3.95, set tea £6.95
Open all year, every day,
9am – 10.30pm, afternoon
tea served 3pm – 5.30pm
1 2 3 &

DROITWICH   Hereford and Worcester   Map 03 SO86

**Château Impney
Hotel**
Tel (0905) 774411

A late 19th-century replica of a French château standing in 65 acres of landscaped grounds, Château Impney provides an opportunity to relax over afternoon tea in truly elegant surroundings. There is attentive service by professional staff, who can offer a good selection of cakes, scones and gâteaux – all made here.

Pot of tea £1.25
Open all year, every day,
2.30 – 6pm (for tea)
Meals available

DROITWICH   Hereford and Worcester   Map 03 SO86

Raven Hotel
St Andrews Street
Tel (0905) 772224

Convenient for the centre of Droitwich, the Raven has a very pleasant and comfortable lounge in which to enjoy afternoon tea. Tea is served with professional propriety by attentive staff, and a good selection of cakes, gâteaux and scones are all homemade.

Pot of tea £1.25
Open all year, every day,
2.30 – 6pm (for tea)
Meals available
1 2 3

DRYBURGH   Borders *Berwickshire*   Map 12 NT53

Dryburgh Abbey Hotel Tel (0835) 22261	A charming red sandstone house situated in its own delightful grounds and gardens alongside the River Tweed and by the famous Abbey. The comfortable lounge is a perfect setting for afternoon tea. Homebaked cakes, scones and sandwiches are served.	Set tea £2.95 Open all year, every day, 8am – midnight [1] [2] [3]

DUFFTOWN   Speyside   *Banffshire*   Map 15 NJ45

Taste of Speyside 10 Balvenie Street Tel (0340) 20860	This is a 'Taste of Scotland' restaurant, tartan carpeted with large round wooden tables. Excellent homemade cakes, scones and biscuits are available with specialities such as heather honey and malt whisky cheesecake. Our inspector particularly enjoyed the whisky cake. Pancakes are made to order and a choice of tea blends is offered.	Pot of tea 50p Open Mar – Oct, every day, 11am – 6pm Good lunches are served [1] [3]

DULVERTON   Somerset   Map 03 SS92

Ashwick House Tel (0398) 23868	Standing on the edge of Exmoor, this charming house is set in six acres of beautiful grounds overlooking the River Barle valley. Afternoon tea, served in fine bone china, can be taken in one of the three comfortable lounges – where fires burn invitingly during the colder months – or on the terrace with its fine views across the surrounding countryside. All the food is homemade and the range of teas usually includes some rarer blends for the connoisseur, such as Imperial Gold China tea. The service is friendly and efficient and owners the Sherwood family are often on hand to welcome their visitors.	Tea and biscuits 75p, Set tea £1.75 Open all year, every day, 3 – 5.30pm

DULVERTON   Somerset   Map 03 SS92

Carnarvon Arms Hotel
Tel (0398) 23302

An early Victorian hotel situated on the edge of Exmoor. There are a number of comfortable lounges and a garden where one might take tea. Blazing log fires in winter, fresh flowers and deep armchairs all contribute to the enjoyment of memorable homemade cakes, scones, biscuits, jam and Somerset clotted cream. Herb tea and Earl Grey are offered as alternatives to the standard blend.

Tea 80p, cream tea £2.50 (£3.10 with cakes) Open all year (ex 3 wks Feb), every day, 3.30pm – 5.30pm

1   3

DUMFRIES   Dumfries and Galloway   *Dumfriesshire* Map 11 NX97

The Old Bank Restaurant
94 Irish Street
Tel (0387) 53499

A former bank now converted to an elegant and comfortable restaurant serving morning coffee, light lunches and afternoon teas. There is a large selection of tempting homemade scones, cakes and speciality puddings – the toffee banana pie being particularly good!   A choice of tea blends is served in stainless steel pots.

Pot of tea 55p
Open all year (ex 2 wks Christmas), Tue – Sat, 10am – 5pm
Light lunches

DUMFRIES   Dumfries and Galloway   *Dumfriesshire* Map 11 NX97

Oliver's Coffee Shop
135 High Street
Tel (0387) 53499

Friendly, self-service High Street franchise Homemade, though rather commercial looking cakes, scones and sandwiches are served. A choice of tea blends is offered, and tea is served with a pottery teapot and mug, individual jugs of milk and sugar sachets.

Pot of tea 50p
Open all year every day, 8am – 5pm

DUNBLANE   Central   *Perthshire*   Map 11 NN70

Cromlix House
Kinbuck
Tel (0786) 822125

This distinguished country house has lost none of its atmosphere in the transition from family seat to hotel. Situated close to the village of Kinbuck, off the B 8033, 3 miles north east of Dunblane, the hotel still forms part of the 5000 acre estate. The public rooms are comfortable, containing many fine antiques and paintings, and log fires blazing in the grates in colder months create a homely atmosphere. Afternoon tea may either be taken in the Morning Room or in the recently restored Edwardian conservatory. All the scones, biscuits and jams in the set tea are homemade, and served by polite, young staff.

Afternoon tea £5
Open all year (except 2 weeks Feb), every day, 2 – 5pm

1   2   3

DUNKELD   Tayside *Perthshire*   Map 11 N004

**Stakis Dunkeld
House Hotel**
Tel (03502) 771

A smartly refurbished hotel which is part of a leisure and time-share complex. The hotel stands on the banks of the Tay in 280 acres of grounds. Teas are served in the comfortable foyer-lounge. The selection offered ranges from tea and biscuits to open sandwiches, and the set tea comprises sandwiches, homemade scones and cakes. A range of tea blends is offered.

Tea and biscuits £1.25, set afternoon tea £5.50
Open all year, every day, 9.30am – 5.30pm, afternoon tea is served 3pm – 5.30pm

1 2 .3 &

DUNSTER   Somerset   Map 03 SS94

The Tea Shoppe
3 High Street
Tel (0643) 821304

Built in 1495 the Tea Shoppe is the only brick faced building in the High Street. The interior is olde worlde style with polished tables and lots of plants. The display counter is said to have come from Dunster Castle. Homemade cakes include carrot cake, Dunster tutti frutti, Somerset cider cake and Bramley apple cake. Herb, Indian and China teas are served.

Tea 50p – 60p, scone tea £1.80, Dunster cream tea £2
Open Mar – Oct and 22 Dec – 1 Jan, Mon – Sun, 9.30am – 6pm (open weekends Nov – 22 Dec)

DURHAM   Co Durham   Map 12 NZ24

Bowes Brasserie
Royal County Swallow
Hotel
Old Elvet
Tel 091 – 386 6821

A comfortable venue with friendly service where a small choice of teas is available. Tea is well presented in a china teapot with lots of hot water. Sandwiches, cheese scones, sweet scones, cream cakes and Danish pastries are served.

Pot of tea 90p – 95p, set afternoon tea £4
Open Jan – Dec, every day, 10am – 9.30 afternoon break menu served 3.30pm – 5.30pm
Lunch and dinner

1 2 3 &

DURHAM   Co Durham   Map 12 NZ24

Treats
27 – 28 Silver Street
Tel 091 – 384 5620

A first-floor, self-service tearoom off the pedestrian walkway in the city centre. Treats offers a good selection of homemade goodies such as lemon meringue pie, Dutch apple pie, chocolate nut crunch and rum fudge log. There are also scones, pastries, savoury flans, filled rolls and sandwiches. Standard blend, Earl Grey and English Breakfast teas are available.

Pot of tea 38p
Open Jan – Dec, Mon – Sat, 9am – 4.15pm
Light lunches

EAGLESHAM   Strathclyde *Renfrewshire*   Map 11 NS55

Wishing Well
63 Montgomery Street
Tel (03553) 2774

A friendly, popular teashop where homebaking is the speciality. The converted cottages make for a homely atmosphere with a real fire, plain painted walls and pictures for sale. There is a wide selection of homebaked scones, teabreads and cakes – all very tempting and at reasonable prices. While there is no choice of tea blends, tea is well presented in traditional teapots with bone china crockery.

Pot of tea 50p (£1.50 buys a good tea)
Open all year Tue – Sun, 10am – 5pm

EARDISLAND   Herefordshire   Map 03 SO45

Eardisland **Tearooms and** **Garden** Church Lane Tel (05447) 226	A pretty cottage in the picturesque Tudor village. Tea is served in the conservatory with additional seating in the attractive garden when weather permits. The cottage is also a gift and craft shop with an abundance of tourist information. Homemade scones, cakes and pastries are served from attractive crockery. Light snacks are available and picnic food is sold to take out.	Pot of tea 40p, set tea £1.40 Open all year, every day, 11am – 6pm Snack meals 1

EASINGWOLD   North Yorkshire   Map 08 SE56

Truffles Snowdon House Spring Street Tel (0347) 22342	Situated in the centre of this picturesque Yorkshire village, the tearoom is part of a delicatessen shop. The proprietors also specialise in outside catering. A large selection of pastries and cakes are served in the pretty pine-furnished room. Hot dishes of the day and sandwiches are also available. A choice of five tea blends is offered and tea is made in stainless steel pots.	Pot of tea 50p – 75p, set afternoon tea £2.95 Open all year, Mon – Sat, 9am – 5.30pm Tue – Thu, 9.30am – 5pm Mon and Sat

---

EASTBOURNE   East Sussex   Map 05 TV69

Chatsworth Coffee **Lounge** 5 Chatsworth Walk Cornfield Road Tel (0323) 26169.	Conveniently situated for shopping, this is a popular contemporary coffee shop with a good selection of filter coffees and choice of teas. Snack meals include Welsh rarebit, ploughmans lunch and fresh sandwiches. An assortment of cakes, biscuits and teabreads is also served by efficient uniformed staff.	Tea and cake £1.50 Open all year, Mon – Sat, 8.30am – 4.30pm Snack meals

---

ECCLESHALL   Staffordshire   Map 07 SO72

St George Hotel Castle Street Tel (0785) 850300	A busy town centre hotel with green and white façade and olde worlde interior: exposed beams, inglenook fireplace and polished brass tables. Morning coffee and afternoon tea are served throughout the day in the bar area or, in the summer, one may sit outside. Scones, gâteaux and teacakes are served, and a choice of tea blends is available.	Pot of tea 45p, set afternoon tea £2 Open all year, every day, 10.30am – 11pm 1 2 3

EDDLESTON   Borders *Peebleshire*   Map 11 NT27

The Scots Pine Cottage Bank Tel (072 13) 365	A single storey building situated on the A703 just north of the village and five miles from Peebles. Homemade cakes, fruit slices, toffee shortbread and apple pie are featured on the menu as well as hot and cold meals and vegetarian dishes. The set tea comprises cakes, scones and sandwiches.	Set tea £2.10 (£1.35 without sandwiches), high tea £4.50 Open all year, every day, 9am – 5pm Lunches

EDINBURGH   Lothian *Midlothian*   Map 11 NT27

Caledonian Hotel Princes Street Tel (031) 2252433	Built on the site of the old Caledonian Railway Station, this distinguished building now houses a superb hotel. Traditional afternoon tea here is served in the large and gracious lounge by smart, professional and friendly staff. A good variety of well-prepared cakes, freshly-cut sandwiches, scones and muffins is available, as well as a choice of tea blends and herbal infusions.	Full tea £5.25 and à la carte Open all year, every day, 3 – 5.30pm (for afternoon tea) Meals available 1 2 3

ELLESMERE   Shropshire   Map 07 SJ33

Tudor Cottage Teashop 31 Scotland Street	Tea is served in the front room of this half-timbered Tudor cottage which has a wealth of charm and character. There is a large inglenook fireplace, exposed beams and an abundance of brass and bric-à-brac. Cinnamon toast, crumpets, scones and cakes are available and leaf tea is made in an earthenware pot with china crockery and a strainer provided. Eleven blends of tea are offered.	Pot of tea 45p, set teas £2 Open all year, every day, 9am – 7pm Hot and cold snack meals

ELY   Cambridgeshire   Map 05 TL58

Steeplegate 16–18 High Street Tel (0353) 664731	These tearooms are situated above a craft shop and divided into smoking and non-smoking parts. It is a characterful building with sloping floors and bare tables. Homebaking is a feature of the menu which offers a selection of biscuits, cakes, gâteaux, cheesecakes, scones and teacakes. A choice of tea blends is available.	Tea 45p, scone 75p Open all year. Wed – Sat and Mon, 10am – 5pm

ELY   Cambridgeshire   Map 05 TL58

Tea For Two 8 St Marys Street Tel (0353) 665011	On the main street with leaded window exterior, the décor of this teashop is simple with pink clothed tables, pine wheelbacked chairs and pink and grey china. There is a display shelf with a range of homemade cakes, pastries, scones, shortbread, apple pie and gingerbread men. Well-flavoured leaf tea is served and a variety of blends is offered.	Tea 70p, set tea £2.95 Open all year, every day, 9.30am – 5.30pm

ETTINGTON   Warwickshire   Map 04 SP24

School House Banbury Road Tel (0789) 151	An attractive stone-built house by the school in the centre of the village. Tea is served in the pretty lounge where crafts are displayed for sale. The tearoom is furnished in pine with Nottingham lace cloths and delicate china. A range of homebaked cakes, fruit pies, scones and shortbread is available and tea is presented in the traditional way with loose leaves and hot water.	Cream tea £1.60, set tea £2.40 Open all year, Tue – Sat, 10am – 5.30pm (5pm winter), Sun 2pm – 5.30pm (5pm winter) Light lunches

EVESHAM   Hereford & Worcester   Map 04 SP04

Diamonds
53 High Street
Tel (0386) 2293

This restaurant has a shop front type exterior, simple décor: plain walls with prints, clothed tables and a counter area with a small display of homemade cakes and scones. There is a full menu including some snack items, served by friendly, welcoming staff.

Tea 50p, set tea £1.60
Open all year, Mon –
Sat, 9am – 5.30pm
Lunch and dinner

[1] [2] [3]

EXETER   Devon   Map 03 SX99

Tinleys of Exeter
Cathedral Close
Tel (0392) 72865

This listed building, thought to be Exeter's oldest tearoom, stands in a delightful position opposite the Cathedral. It was built on the site of the St Michael's Gate and remains of the original inner city wall can still be seen on the ground floor. The cosy, beamed tearoom adjoins the Harvester Bakery where the delicious bread and cakes, as well as dishes for the first floor restaurant, are made. There is a wide selection of pastries, toasts and tea breads as well as the set Devon cream tea, and also a continental breakfast, available all day!

Pot of tea from 60p, cream tea £2.00
Open all year, Mon – Sat, 8.30am – 6.00pm
Hot meals in restaurant

[1] [3]

FAKENHAM   Norfolk   Map 09 TF92

Acorns Coffee Shop
Aldiss Department
Store
Market Place
Tel (0328) 4554

A split level coffee shop on the second floor of the department store. Not suitable for the disabled as the stairs are numerous. A pink carpet with pine furniture creates a cosy atmosphere. Light snacks and meals are available all day, and cakes and pastries are all homemade. A choice of tea blends is offered.

Pot of tea 46p
Open all year (except Christmas), Mon – Sat, 9.15am – 4.30pm
Lunch

FAKENHAM   Norfolk   Map 09 TF92

Pensthorpe Waterfowl Trust
Norwich Road
Tel (0328) 51465

After many years of work this park was finally opened in 1988. As well as the wildfowl to see, the old flint farm buildings have been restored to create an exhibition hall, gift shop and tearoom. A good selection of homemade cakes, pastries and light snacks are available on a self-service basis. Smoking is not permitted.

Cakes 40p, scone with jam and cream 70p
Open Easter – Dec, very day, 10am – 6pm
Lunches
[&]

FAKENHAM   Norfolk   Map 09 TF92

Tricia's Tea Rooms
5 Cattle Market Street
Tel (0328) 55004

This pretty teashop is well worth seeking out in a small street behind the market. The atmosphere is warm and cheerful, and owners David and Tricia Evsden are always on hand should you need assistance in choosing from the excellent range of teas, all naturally flavoured. The tempting array of homemade cakes is beautifully presented on fine china. No smoking is permitted.

Pot of tea 55p
Open all year, except Christmas, every day 9.30am – 5pm
Light lunches served all day

CHIVERS

ENJOY THE REAL TASTE OF TRADITIONAL JELLY FRUIT CONFECTIONERY COMBINED WITH THE FINEST TASTE OF CHIVERS QUALITY

Fresh Thinking
FROM
TY·PHOO

YOU ONLY GET AN 'OO' WITH TY·PHOO

FALKLAND   Fife *Cupar*   Map 11 NO41

Kind Kyttock's Kitchen .
Cross Wynd
Tel (0337) 57477

Situated in an historic former vicarage close to the Falkland Palace, this characteristic tearoom takes its name from the heroine of a poem by Scots poet, William Dunbar. Kind Kyttock settled in Falkland and one of her virtues was serving refreshments to weary travellers. The ballad is printed in full inside the menu. The tearoom is on two floors, decorated with paintings and ornaments and features several loudly ticking clocks – all showing the wrong time!

There is a good range of loose leaf tea and an extensive menu of homemade cakes and shortbreads, including Scot's pancakes, Isle of Rhum gingerbread and Campbell fudge cake. The licensed restaurant also serves light meals.

Special tea 70p, cream tea £2.65
Open Feb – Christmas Eve, every day, 10.30am – 5.30pm
Snacks and light lunches

FALMOUTH   Cornwall & Isles of Scilly   Map 02 SW83

de Wynns
55 Church Street
Tel (0326) 319259

Traditional style teashop overlooking the harbour with heavy print wallpaper, wooden tables, bow backed chairs, settles and benches. There are many antique pieces and objects of interest. Food is served from attractive willow patterned plates. Mostly homemade cakes, scones and teabreads are served. Lunches, toasted sandwiches and snack foods are available.

Cup of tea 40p, set tea £1.70
Open all year, Mon – Sat, 10am – 5pm
Lunches

FALMOUTH   Cornwall & Isles of Scilly   Map 02 SW83

Cavendish Coffee House
12 Market Street
Tel (0326) 319438

A pleasant coffee house with exposed beams, soft lighting, light oak chairs and pretty table cloths. There is a comprehensive menu and a fine display of homemade cakes and pastries in the window. Eight tea varieties are offered, served in china pots with milk or lemon.

Pot of tea 50p – 55p, cream tea £2.25
Open all year, every day, 9am – 5.30pm
Light lunches

FARNHAM   Surrey   Map 04 SO84

The Bush Hotel
The Borough
Tel (0252) 715237

Tea is served in the open lounge area with coffee tables and attractive décor in keeping with the traditional style of the hotel. A selection of tea varieties is offered and a range of pastries, cakes and scones is served by courteous staff.

Tea 90p
Open Jan – Dec, every day, 10am – 10pm, afternoon tea served 2pm – 6pm
[1] [2] [3]

FARNHAM   Surrey   Map 04 SO84

The Garden
Restaurant
The Redgrave Theatre
Brightwells, East Street
Tel (0252) 716601

A pleasant airy restaurant located inside the Redgrave theatre overlooking the gardens, with fresh décor and pretty lace table cloths. A choice of teas is offered with homemade scones and cakes, gateaux and teacakes.

Pot of tea 40p
Open all year, Mon –
(half day Mon), 10am –
8pm, tea served 3pm –
5pm

[1] [3]

FOCHABERS   Grampian *Morayshire*   Map 15 NJ35

The Gallery
85 High Street
Tel (0343) 820981

Small coffee shop area to rear of a gift shop, simply furnished with wooden tables and stools, and additional seating in the garden. Paintings are hung for sale. There is a selection of homemade cakes, biscuits and scones and a choice of tea blends. Smoking is not permitted.

Pot of tea 50p
Open all year, Mon – Sat
Sun, 9am – 5pm

[1] [2] [3]

FOCHABERS   Grampian *Morayshire*   Map 15 NJ35

Spey Restaurant
Visitor Centre
Baxters of Speyside
Tel (0343) 820393

New bright, spacious self-service restaurant, part of the Baxters Visitor Centre. Lunches and high teas are served, and a selection of homemade scones, teabreads, biscuits and cakes are available. Baxters pancakes are cooked to order.

Pot of tea 40p
Open 24 Mar – 27 Oct,
Mon – Fri, 10am – 4.30pm,
Easter weekend, Sat – Sun
13 May – 10 Sep (Sat.11am
– 5.30pm, Sun 12.30pm –
4.30pm)
Christmas shopping
weekends

[&]

FOLKINGHAM   Lincolnshire   Map 08 TF13

Quaintways
17 Market Place
Tel (05297) 416

A lovely little teashop in an interesting village, full of local history. The proprietress provides friendly and attentive service. Light lunches and afternoon teas are served with a choice of tea blends and a good range of home baking.

Pot of tea 45p – 50p, set
teas £1.75 – £2.75
Open Apr – Sep, Thu –
Sun, noon – 5pm
Lunches

FORRES Grampian *Morayshire* Map 14 NJO5

Busters Bistro
39 High Street
Tel (0309) 75541

Bright, lively bistro with art deco theme and pine tables and chairs. There is a small range of homemade scones, teabreads and cakes, and tea is served in a stainless steel pot.

Pot of tea 45p, cream tea £1.45
Open all year, every day, 9.30am – 11pm
1 2 3

FRAMPTON Dorset Map 03 SY79

Gatehouse
7 Dorchester Road
Tel (0300) 20280

Village post office with tea shop, part of which dates from the 17th century. It is a small, cosy room with pine furniture, plants and pictures, where scones, cakes and pastries are served by the friendly proprietress. Smoking is not permitted.

Teas £1.10 – £1.80
Open Jan – Dec, Tue – Sat, 9am – 5.30pm

FRASERBURGH Grampian *Aberdeenshire* Map 15 NJ96

Ritchie's Coffee Shop
30 Cross Street
Tel (0346) 2774

Attractive, freshly decorated and clean coffee shop. Although a simple operation it offers good home baking in pleasant surroundings – a scarce commodity in this north-east corner of Scotland. No smoking is permitted.

Pot of tea 55p
Open Jan – Dec, Mon – Tue and Thu – Sat, 9am – 4.30pm

GALASHIELS Borders *Selkirkshire* Map 12 NT43

Sanders Restaurant
94A High Street
Tel (0896) 56055

A charming little restaurant, once a tailoring workshop which is reflected in the pictures on the walls. The atmosphere is warm and friendly, and whether you sample the traditional afternoon tea, high tea or a hot meal you will know that it is all good home cooking.

Pot of tea 30p, set tea £2
Open Jan – Dec, every day, 10am – 8pm weekdays, 10am – 10.30pm Thu – Sat, 3pm – 8pm Sun
Lunch, high tea, supper
1 3

GATEHOUSE OF FLEET Dumfries & Galloway *Kirkcudbrightshire* Map 11 NX55

Bobbin Coffee Shop
36 High Street
Tel (055 74) 229

The dining room of a listed guesthouse. A light, airy room to the rear of the High Street property. Very homely with a selection of very good home baking. Smoking is not permitted.

Pot of tea 55p
Open Jan – Dec, Tue – Sat, 10.15am – 2pm (10am – 4pm July – Aug)
1 3

GLASGOW   Strathclyde *Lanarkshire*   Map 11 NS56

The Willow Tea Room 217 Sauchiehall Street Tel 041 332 0521	This building which once housed the famous Willow Tearoom (1904) has been restored to the original designs of architect Charles Rennie Mackintosh and is furnished with contemporary tables and chairs also of his design. The delightful décor is complemented by the smart black and white uniforms of the waitresses. The tearoom is situated on the first floor and entry is through the small shop below.	Pot of tea 55p, afternoon tea £3.55 Open all year, Mon – Sat, 9.30am – 4.30pm Light lunches available

---

GLASTONBURY   Somerset   Map 03 ST53

The Willows Tearooms Shapwick Road Westhay Tel (04586) 389	Part of the Willows Peat Company which also includes a garden centre and visitor centre with displays of the story of peat. The tearoom is pretty with bright green furniture and oil cloths and there is additional seating in the garden. There is a Light Bite menu with vegetarian dishes and traditional afternoon tea fare, all fresh and homemade.	Cream tea £1.95 Open all year (ex Christmas and New Year), every day 10am – 6pm (5pm winter) Light meals

GLOUCESTER   Gloucestershire   Map 03 SO81

Seasons Restaurant & Teahouse 52 College Court, off Westgate Street	Situated in a narrow lane off a main street and adjacent to St Michaels Gate, this is a large, light tearoom with feature windows, clothed tables and wooden furniture. Lunch is served, with a good selection of vegetarian dishes and light snacks. A choice of homebaked scones, cakes, Continental pastries and American desserts is offered, and a variety of tea blends.	Tea 55p Open all year, Mon – Sat, 10am – 5.30pm Lunch ⬜1

GOSFORTH   Cumbria   Map 11 NY00

The Lakeland Habit Tel (09405) 232	An open staircase from a stationers and a country clothing shop leads to this attractive and comfortable tearoom – a converted warehouse which retains its original pulley and hoist. Tempting choices include cakes, gâteaux, cheesecakes, sandwiches and warm scones with Cumberland rum butter. Good quality teas (choice of blends) are served by friendly staff – an excellent place to stop.	Pot of tea 50p – 55p, Traditional afternoon tea £2.75 Open all year, every day, 9.30am – 7pm (closes 5.30pm from Whitsun – Nov)

GRANGE-OVER-SANDS   Cumbria   Map 07 SD47

The Cedar Tree Yewbarrow Terrace Tel (04484) 32511	The Cedar Tree occupies part of a gift shop in a parade of shops, and offers a very good leaf tea served in china teapots. There is a range of scones and cakes with combinations of cream, jam, rum butter etc. Homemade cakes, honey, marmalade and rum butter are on sale at the counter.	Pot of tea 50p, set afternoon tea £1.25 – £1.85 Open all year, every day, 9.30am – 5pm Lunches available

---

GRANTHAM   Lincolnshire   Map 08 SK93

Catlins
11 High Street
Tel (0476) 590345

This is an historic building worthy of note. Built in 1560, much of the original facework and interior beams are still to be seen. In 1740 Grantham Gingerbread was first made in a bakery to the rear and is still served today made to the original recipe. A range of fancy cakes, scones, teacakes and sandwiches is served by friendly staff.

Pot of tea 48p, cream tea £1.75
Open Jan – Dec, Mon – Sat, 9am – 5pm
1

GRANTHAM   Lincolnshire   Map 08 SK93

Knightingales
Guildhall Street
Tel (0476) 79243

A small, friendly self-service establishment, popular throughout the day for morning coffee, light lunches and afternoon tea. All home baking, specialising in wholefood and vegetarian dishes. The carrot and cinnamon cake enjoyed by our inspector is a particular favourite. There is a comprehensive choice of speciality teas, served in a china pot with matching crockery.

Pot of tea 35p – 40p, cakes 35p – 95p
Open all year (ex bank holidays), Mon – Sat, 9.30am – 4.30pm

GRANTOWN-ON-SPEY   Highland *Morayshire*   Map 14 NJ02

Coffee & Ice Cream Parlour
32–35 High Street
Tel (0479) 2001

Despite the name, this establishment offers much more than ice cream and coffee. As well as a range of hot dishes and salads, a good selection of leaf teas can be enjoyed with home baking and quality gâteaux. Tea is made in china teapots and served with fresh milk.

Pot of tea 40p – 60p, cakes from 40p
Open Jan – Oct and Dec, Mon – Sat, 9am – 5pm or 7pm
Lunch

GREAT BIRCHAM   Norfolk   Map 0G TF74

Bircham Windmill
Tel (048523) 393

The self-service tearooms are part of a small complex comprising the windmill, bakery and stables. Homemade cakes are served with a fresh pot of tea. Traditionally baked loaves are also for sale along with a range of gift items.

Pot of tea 35p, cream tea £1.50
Open 20 May – 20 Sep, Sun – Fri, from Easter Wed and Sun

GRIMSBY   Humberside   Map 08 TA20

The Larder
39 Bethlehem Street
Tel (0472) 361867

On two floors behind a provisions shop (coffee and tea a speciality), this coffee and teashop is inviting and comfortable with large round tables and matching wheelback chairs. Light lunches are served, and a selection of sandwiches, homebaked, cakes, pastries and gateaux, with an extensive range of teas and coffees.

Pot of tea 50p
Open Jan – Dec, Mon – Sat, 9am – 4.30pm
Light lunches

GUILDFORD   Surrey   Map 04 SU94

Next Cafe
White Lion Walk
Tel (0483) 579942

A light, airy contemporary establishment located in a shopping arcade within the Next store. Scones, cakes, gâteaux and pastries are served with a selection of tea blends

Pot of tea 55p, afternoon tea £2.20
Open all year, Mon – Sat, 8.30am – 5pm

GWEEK   Cornwall & Scilly Isles   Map 02 SW85

Gweek Tea Gardens
Tel (032622) 635

A listed period cottage in the creek-side village famed for its seal sanctuary. Children are welcome here where the theme is unmistakingly The Lord Of The Rings. The tearoom is simply furnished and decorated with Hobbit paraphernalia. Ideal budget eating for the family, with hot and cold meals, homemade scones, cakes and pastries.

Cream tea £1.50
Open Easter – Sep, every day, 9am – 8pm
Hot meals

HADDINGTON   Lothian   *East Lothian*   Map 12 NT57

Peter Potter Gallery
10 The Sands (off Church Street)
Tel (062082) 2080

A popular rendezvous for locals, this 'no smoking' teashop serves a delicious array of home-baked cakes including lemon cake, apple cake, date crumble, biscuits, scones and croissants. Tea is served in local pottery teapots with a choice of speciality blends and herbal infusions. The gallery and bookshop offer additional interest.

Pot of tea 46p, cakes 15p – 65p
Open all year, Mon – Sat, 10am – 5pm, Thu 10am – 2pm, closed Sun
Light lunches 12 noon – 2pm

HADLEIGH   Suffolk   Map 05 TM04

Odds and Ends
131 High Street
Tel (0473) 822032

This delightful teashop, with the appearance and atmosphere of a private house, has a lovely old cast-iron fireplace and an old copper boiler on display. Good home cooking provides inexpensive, tasty meals, and a tempting display of cakes includes date and walnut, chocolate and fruit cakes. Tea is served in functional brown pottery in keeping with the surroundings.

Set tea £2
Open all year, every day, 10am – 6pm
Lunch
1

HALLAND   East Sussex   Map 05 TQ41

The Coffee Shop
Halland Forge Hotel
Tel (082584) 456

Situated on the A22 with excellent car parking facilities, this modern fully-licensed coffee shop has a cafeteria-style buffet and self-service counter. Homemade Sussex cream teas, buttered scones, iced sponges and freshly made sandwiches are available.

Set tea £1.65
Open daily, 8am – 6pm
Breakfast, morning coffee, lunch

HAMBLE   Hampshire   Map 04 SY40

The Village Tea Rooms
High Street
Tel (0703) 455683

Two years ago Mr Jenkin, the proprietor, left the *QE2* as shops manager and turned his hand to converting this former rope makers/coffin makers into a cosy tearoom. The old building, full of character, dates from about 1640. There is a variety of tempting cakes, and a selection of tea blends, as well as friendly, courteous service.

Cream tea £1.55
Open all year, Mon – Fri 9am – 5.30pm (5pm in winter), Sat – Sun 9am – 7pm (6pm in winter)

HANBURY   Hereford and Worcester   Map 07 SO06

The Jinney Ring Restaurant
Tel (052784) 653

This ancient barn, transported piece by piece from its former site and painstakingly rebuilt here as a tearoom and restaurant, is part of a craft workshop complex. Cakes, scones, full or snack meals, served by pleasant staff, is accompanied by a traditional pot of tea with a choice of speciality blends available.

Pot of tea 40p, set tea £3.50
Open all year, Wed – Sun and bank holidays 10.30am – 5pm
Lunch
1   3   &

HARLECH   Gwynedd   Map 06 SH53

Bwtri Bach
Stryd Fawr

Situated close to the Castle, Bwtri Bach forms part of a delicatessen in the village centre. The large stone fireplace, stone floor and pretty tablecloths provide a pleasant setting for afternoon tea. Tempting homemade cakes, scones and rolls, displayed on an old shop counter, are served by friendly staff. There is a good range of Welsh cheeses for sale.

Open all year, Mon – Sat 9.30am – 4.30pm, closed Sun

HARLECH   Gwynedd   Map 06 SH53

The Plas
High Street
Tel (0766) 780204

Enjoying one of the finest views in Harlech, the café (part of a restaurant, crafts and gallery complex) is decorated in conservatory style with a grassed terrace for summer use. Traditional pots of tea, pastries, scones and a range of cakes (some homemade) are served by efficient staff.

Pot of tea 55p, cakes and pastries 50p – 80p
Open all year, daily, 9am – 8pm
Lunch, dinner
1

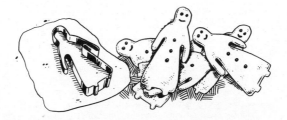

HARROGATE   North Yorkshire   Map 08 SE35

Betty's Café Tea Rooms
1 Parliament Street
Tel (0423) 64659

Overlooking Montpellier Gardens, Betty's, founded by a Swiss confectioner in 1919, is famous throughout Yorkshire and beyond, and three further branches of the tearooms have now also been opened (see entries under Ilkley, Northallerton and York). No visitor to Harrogate should miss this experience. Everything is freshly baked on the premises, using a unique combination of Swiss and traditional Yorkshire recipes, and you will simply be spoilt for choice. For a real Yorkshire treat, though, you could try one of Betty's special rich fruit cakes with a slice of Wensleydale cheese as an accompaniment. The range of tea blends leaves nothing to be desired. In the evenings there are café concerts.

Pot of tea from £1.08, cream tea £3.05
Open all year, every day, 9am – 9pm
Hot meals also served
1 2 3

HATHERSAGE   Derbyshire   Map 08 SK28

Corner Cupboard Café
Main Road
Tel (0433) 50770

Bow windows look out onto the main street, and at the rear there is a garden for teas in summer. In the upstairs room there is a permanent White Elephant stall, with the proceeds going to a local charity. Cream teas and full afternoon teas are served, the cakes are homemade and there is a choice of blends of tea.

Pot of tea 40 – 50p, cakes from 45p, cream tea £1.95, full afternoon tea £2.30
Open every day, Mon – Fri 10am – 6pm, Sat and Sun 9am – 7.30pm
Breakfast and light lunch also served

HAVERFORDWEST   Dyfed   Map 02 SM91

Rendezvous Coffee Shop
Ocky White
Department Store
7 Bridge Street
Tel (0437) 2781

A clean, modern coffee shop situated in a department store. The self-service counter offers doughnuts, custard slices, assorted pastries, sandwiches and a salad bar. There is a choice of traditional or lemon tea.

Pot of tea and pastry £1.20
Open all year, Mon – Sat, 9am – 5.30pm
3

HAWKCHURCH   Devon   Map 03 ST30

Fairwater Head Hotel
Tel (02977) 349

Set in beautiful gardens with glorious views, this warm and friendly country house hotel offers traditional afternoon tea served either on the patio or in the garden lounge. Dorset and West Country recipes provide the basis for home-baked fruit cakes, flapjacks, carrot cake, and shortbread; the tea (there is a choice of blends) is served in fine china teapots.

Set tea £1.50
Open Mar – Dec, daily, 2.30pm – 5pm

1 2 3

HEACHAM   Norfolk   Map 09 TF63

Norfolk Lavender Caley Mill Tel (0485) 70384	Stop for tea here to enjoy home-baked cakes and cream teas amid a field of scented lavender at England's only lavender farm, and home of the National Collection of Lavender. The self-service Miller's Cottage Tea Room with tea lawn is run by chatty local ladies who serve tea in a pretty blue patterned china service.	Pot of tea 50p, cream tea £1.10 Open Easter to spring bank holiday, daily 2.30pm – 5pm Spring bank holiday – Oct daily 10.30am – 5pm Nov – Christmas, Mon – Sat 10.30am – 5pm

---

HELSTON   Cornwall and Isles of Scilly   Map 02 SW62

The Handy Shop Sithney Tel (03265) 573545	This simply furnished tearoom is behind a Cornish stone cottage just one mile from the Helston to Penzance road. Mrs Langford has served tea and homemade cakes here for 19 years, and the atmosphere is very friendly and chatty. Scones, rock cakes, lemon sponge and iced fancies are just some of the cakes available.	Plain tea £1.15, cream tea £1.45 Open Easter – Sep, daily, 9am – 6pm

---

HENLEY-ON-THAMES   Oxfordshire   Map 04 SU78

Red Lion Hotel Hart Street Tel (0491) 572161	Henley's famous Red Lion Hotel stands at one end of the old arched bridge over the River Thames. Traditional afternoon and cream teas are served in the two comfortable lounges by professional staff. Sandwiches, teacakes, scones and pastries are all good, and the pots of tea are well flavoured, with a choice of Indian, Ceylon, Darjeeling or Earl Grey.	Full afternoon tea £5.50 Open every day, 3pm – 6pm 1 2 3

HOLLINGBOURNE   Kent   Map 05 TQ85

Great Danes Ashford Road Tel (0622) 30022	A popular and friendly hotel with extensive facilities, including the pleasant Garden Café which serves a traditional afternoon tea of toasted teacakes, gâteaux, scones and sandwiches accompanied by a fresh pot of tea. Alternatively, tea can be served in the lobby lounge.	Pot of tea 70p, afternoon tea £2.75 Open all year, daily, Garden Café 10am – 11pm, afternoon tea served 3pm – 6pm; in lounge 2.30pm – 6.30pm. Snacks 1 2 3 &

HOLT   Norfolk   Map 09 TG03

The Mews Chapel Yard Tel (0263) 713968	Teas and light snacks are served in this friendly, small café just off the main high street. Tasty cakes and pastries are supplied by a local baker and cream teas (with a good pot of tea) are available throughout the day. There is a take-away service and a small grill room.	Cream tea £1.20 Open all year, Mon – Sat, 9.30am – 4.30pm Take-away service, grill room

HORLEY   Surrey   Map 04 TQ24

The Chequers Thistle
Brighton Road
Tel (0293) 786992

This Tudor coaching inn, now a friendly hotel, serves traditional tea (with a choice of blends) in the pleasant buttery and by the fireside in the foyer lounge. Homemade sandwiches, quiches and gâteaux are also available.

Pot of tea and biscuits
£1.10
Open all year, daily, 11am – 10.30pm

HOWDEN   Humberside   Map 08 SE72

Bridgegate House Tea and Coffee
15 Bridgegate
Tel (0430) 431010

Situated at the rear of a wholefood shop, this is a small, no smoking tearoom with a tiled floor and simple rough cast walls. Our inspector was amazed at the range of appetising, homemade wholefood cakes and pastries which were available. The tea is freshly made with a choice of blends and herbal infusions.

Pot of tea from 65p, cakes from 55p
Open all year, Mon – Sat, 9am – 4.30pm
Breakfast, morning coffee, light vegetarian lunches
[♿]

HUNGERFORD   Berkshire   Map 04 SU36

The Bear
Charnham Street
Tel (0488) 82512

The cosy Kennet Bar of this 13th-century roadside inn is an ideal place in which to enjoy fresh homemade cakes – including fruit loaf, apple scones and gingerbread – and either a pot of tea or a cup of coffee. In the summer afternoon tea can be served on the terrace.

Pot of tea 65p, cream tea £2.10
Open all year, daily, 3.30pm – 5.30pm

HUNGERFORD   Berkshire   Map 04 SU36

The Tutti Pole
3 High Street
Tel (0488) 82515

Named after an ancient local custom, this teashop has a tempting display of homemade cakes and biscuits which are also on sale to take home. Chocolate crunch, caramel squares and coffee and walnut cake are just some of the choices. A variety of tea blends and coffee is available.

Tutti Pole cream tea £1.95, pot of tea 45p, cakes and biscuits 22p – 52p
Open all year, Mon – Fri 9.30am – 6.30pm, Sat and Sun 9am – 6pm, closed Christmas
[♿]

HUNSTANTON   Norfolk   Map 09 TF64

The Copper Kettle
25 High Street
Tel (04853) 34663

This smart, bright and cheery café in the centre of town serves a good selection of teas, including a substantial afternoon tea of sandwiches, scone and cream, cake, biscuit and a pot of tea.

Pot of tea 40p, cream tea £1.60, afternoon tea £2.30
Open all year, daily, 10am – 5pm, closed Mon in winter

HUNTINGDON Cambridgeshire Map 04 TL27

Old Bridge Hotel Tel (0480) 52681	A large terrace lounge furnished with comfortable sofas and chairs is the setting for afternoon tea at this hotel on the banks of the River Ouse. The range of cakes and pastries on display includes tarts, shortbread, scones and fruit cake and summer fruits in season. The tea is well-made and has a good flavour.	Pot of tea 95p, scones and tea £2.30 Open all year, daily, 2.30pm – 6.30pm 1 2 3

ILKLEY West Yorkshire Map 07 SE14

Betty's Café Tea Rooms 32–34 The Grove Tel (0943) 608029	A traditionally-styled tearoom with stained glass windows and potted plants. Not only does Betty's provide fine teas, but also a good range of light hot dishes, sandwiches, salads, and of course lovely cakes and pastries made in their own Harrogate bakery using Swiss and Yorkshire recipes. Staff are very smart, polite and efficient. See entries for Harrogate, Northallerton, York.	Pot of tea £1.05 – £1.30, cream tea £2.92 Open all year, daily, Mon – Thu 9am – 7pm, Fri – Sun 9am – 9pm Hot meals, salads 1 3

IPSWICH Suffolk Map 05 TM14

Boodles Trading Co Dial Lane Tel (0473) 254241	This small first floor gallery-style teahouse is situated in a listed building in a narrow lane in the town centre. Light toasted snacks, pies, pastries and cakes are available and a choice of eight good quality teas are served in white earthenware teapots with matching milk jug and crockery.	Pot of tea 50p Open all year, Mon – Sat, 9.15am – 4.45pm Snacks

---

KEITH Grampian *Aberdeenshire* Map 15 NJ45

Lunch Box Coffee Shop 121 Mid Street Tel (05422) 2194	This newly decorated coffee shop above a bakers in the main street offers a range of homemade scones, Danish pastries, doughnuts and cakes, and the tea is freshly made. This is a popular place at lunchtime.	Pot of tea 40p Open all year, Mon – Sat, 10am – 4pm Light lunches

---

KEITH Grampian *Aberdeenshire* Map 15 NJ45

The Cottage 142A Mid Street Tel (05422) 7942	This fairly simple cottage-style restaurant in a side street off the main shopping area offers a small selection of homemade scones, biscuits and cakes and freshly made tea.	Pot of tea 30p Open all year, daily, 9am – 4.30pm

---

KESWICK   Cumbria   Map 11 NY22

Bryson's Tearoom
38–42 Main Street
Tel (0596) 72257

A comfortable and spacious tearoom with solid pine tables and chairs, set above the family bakery which supplies the varied selection of cakes. Two set teas – the Lakeland cream tea with rum butter, and the Cumberland Farmhouse tea are available, and traditional tea is served in attractive china. Smoking is not permitted.

Pot of tea 45p – 55p, set teas £2.20 and £2.40
Open Mar – Dec, Mon – Sat, 8.30am – 5.30pm
Breakfast, lunch, dinner

KESWICK   Cumbria   Map 11 NY22

The Rembrandt
25 Station Street
Tel (07687) 72008

Cheery young waitresses serve a good array of homemade cakes and pastries and two set afternoon teas, each with four homemade preserves – lemon curd, plum, strawberry and blackcurrant. This neat unpretentious tearoom also serves meals.

Pot of tea 40p, afternoon tea £1.95 and £2.75
Open all year, daily, 10am – 10pm (Nov – Feb 10am – 7.30pm)
Lunch, dinner, vegetarian meals

KEW   Surrey   Map 05 TQ17

Newens – The Original Maids of Honour
288 Kew Road
Tel (01) 2940 2752

Situated in an attractive building next to Kew Gardens, the entrance to this tearoom is through the shop where cakes and pastries are sold. Pleasant and helpful staff serve a good range of home-baked scones, cakes, gâteaux and sausage rolls and a traditional pot of tea.

Pot of tea 85p, set cream tea £3
Open all year, 10am – 5.30pm, afternoon tea from 2.45pm, closed Sun and Mon afternoon

---

KILCHRENAN   Strathclyde   *Argyllshire*   Map 10 NN02

Ardanaiseig Hotel
Kilchrenan by Taynuilt
Tel (08663) 333

One of Scotland's most famous gardens, noted for its azaleas and rhododendrons, surrounds this fine country-house hotel on the shores of Loch Awe. Visitors to the gardens may round off their afternoon by taking tea in the lovely drawing room overlooking the lawns and the loch. A full afternoon tea, with cucumber sandwiches, scones, cream and raspberry jam, finished by freshly baked cakes, is served with great charm by attentive young staff. To drink, there is a choice of Assam, Earl Grey, Darjeeling or Lapsang Souchong.

Tea and biscuits £1.75, cream tea £2.75, full afternoon tea £3.75
Open mid Apr – late Oct, every day, 3 – 5pm
☐1 ☐2 ☐3

KILDRUMMY   Grampian   *Aberdeenshire*   Map 15 NJ41

Mossat Restaurant
Bridge of Mossat
Tel (09755) 71355

There is a country feel to this restaurant with its beams and floral table cloths, part of a popular gift shop/garden centre. Waitresses serve freshly made tea and a small range of homemade scones, cakes and biscuits.

Pot of tea 40p
Open Mar – Oct, daily,
9.30am – 6.30pm (Nov –
Feb Sat – Sun 9.30am –
6.30pm)
☐1

KINCRAIG   Highland   *Inverness-shire*   Map 14 NH80

Ossian Teashop
Ossian Hotel

A small country hotel has converted an outbuilding into a neat little tearoom with natural stone walls and pine furniture. The tea is freshly made and nicely presented in pottery teapots and the range of homemade cakes and pastries includes Yorkshire cheesecakes, scones and jam, meringues and millionaire shortbread.

Pot of tea 65p and £1,
cakes 15p – 90p
Open Feb – Oct, daily,
10am – 6pm
☐3

KING'S LYNN   Norfolk   Map 09 TF62

Crofters
The Fermoy Centre
King Street
Tel (0553) 773134

This basement café/restaurant has a Continental atmosphere. Date and orange cake, coffee fondant sponge and caramel slices are just a few of the many cakes and pastries on display. The tea is served in a traditional teapot by pleasant waitresses.

Pot of tea 85p
Open all year, Mon – Sat,
9.30am – 5pm
Light snacks, lunch

KING'S LYNN   Norfolk   Map 09 TF62

Duke's Head Coffee Shop
Duke's Head
Tuesday Market Place
Tel (0553) 774996

A modern coffee shop on the front of the centrally situated Duke's Head Hotel. Gâteaux, Danish pastries and scones, prepared by a local bakery, are served with a traditional pot of well-flavoured tea.

Cream tea £1.95
Open all year, daily, 9am –
10.30pm
Morning coffee, light
snacks
☐1 ☐2 ☐3

KINGTON   Hereford and Worcester   Map 03 SO35

Church House
Lyonshall (two miles
from Kington at
junction of A44/A480)
Tel (05448) 350

Church House is a small, Georgian, country
guesthouse standing in its own grounds in the
beautiful Herefordshire countryside. The interior is
decorated in the Edwardian style and authentically
furnished to make a truly delightful setting for
afternoon tea. A wide variety of freshly made scones,
cakes and different blends of tea is always available,
and beautifully served. A full Edwardian afternoon tea
with finger sandwiches can be ordered in advance.
The nearby Church House craft shop displays an
enticing range of Edwardian-style needlecraft and
other giftware. No smoking is permitted.

Pot of tea 60p, cream tea
£1.15
Open Mar – Oct, every
day, 10am – 12noon and 3
– 5.30pm for tea
No smoking in the
tearoom

KINROSS   Tayside   *Kinross-shire*   Map 11 NO10

**Grase and Claret
Restaurant**
Heathery Road
(just west of the M90)
Tel (0577) 64212

This cosy little restaurant enjoys an attractive outlook
across a lake. The home-baking could include apple
and almond cake, scones and chocolate gâteaux and
although the selection is not large, the quality is first
class. The tea is well made, with a choice of blends
and herbal infusions. Homemade fudge and
preserves are for sale.

Pot of tea 40p – 60p, cakes
20p – £1.20
Open Mar – Dec, 9am –
9pm (teas served until
4.30pm)
Lunch, dinner

KIRKCUDBRIGHT   Dumfries and Galloway *Kirkudbrightshire*   Map 11 NX65

The Belfry
39 St Mary Street
Tel (0557) 30861

A combined antique and coffee shop on a corner site
in the main street. Scones, tea breads, and cakes
(some homemade) are available and the tea is served
in a traditional teapot with beautiful Limoges fine
china cups and saucers.

Open Mar – Dec, Mon –
Sat 10am – 5pm, Sun
12.45pm – 5pm

LAGGAN   Highland   *Inverness-shire*   Map 14 NN69

Kiln Room Coffee Shop
Caoldair Pottery
(Nr Laggan Bridge on the A889 Dalwhinnie road)
Tel (05284) 231

This pleasant coffee and tea shop is part of a small pottery and, as you would expect, the teapots, cups and saucers are made here, as are the excellent homemade cakes, available in a large selection which includes coffee, chocolate, apple, spice and carrot cake. Laggan is set in beautiful countryside, with the Monadhliath Mountains to the north, and not far from the Highland Wildlife Park, so the pottery is a convenient port of call for anyone touring the area, and for those looking for an individual souvenir to take home, there is pottery on sale in the showroom.

Pot of tea 50p
Open Easter – Oct every day 9am – 6pm

LAND'S END   Cornwall & Isles of Scilly   Map 02 SW42

The Old Manor House
Sennen
Tel (0736) 871280

The original Land's End Hotel, built around 1790, has a huge inglenook fireplace. The atmosphere is homely and meals are served all day by the jovial proprietors, Mr and Mrs Sedgwick. Homemade scones and traditional Cornish hevva cake are served for tea, with a choice of speciality teas including mixed fruit and mango.

Cream tea £1.75
Open all year (except Christmas), every day, 2pm – 5pm (for tea)
[1] [3]

LAVENHAM   Suffolk   Map 05 TL94

The Swan
High Street
Tel (0787) 247477

Lavenham is probably one of the best surviving examples of a medieval town, and the Swan Hotel is an amalgamation of several old houses, including the Wool Hall and Elizabethan House. The lovely setting is further enhanced by a harpsichord recital each afternoon except Saturday. Cream tea is served with a choice of tea blends, or full afternoon tea comprising finger sandwiches, bridge rolls, scones and a selection of homemade cakes.

Cream tea £3.50, full afternoon tea £5.75
Open all year, every day, tea served 3pm – 5.30pm
[1] [2] [3]

LAVENHAM   Suffolk   Map 05 TL94

Tickle Manor Tearoom
17 High Street
Tel (0787) 248216

A pair of feet and a feather is the sign outside this 16th-century timber-framed house on the high street of this lovely Suffolk town. Cream teas, carrot or banana cake and many other good value items are available, as well as more substantial meals. Some speciality teas are offered and tea is served in a Port Meirion pot. Smoking is not permitted.

Cream tea £2
Open all year (except Christmas), Wed – Mon, 9.30am – 6pm

LEAMINGTON SPA (ROYAL)   Warwickshire   Map 04 SP36

Regency Fayre Restaurant
86 Regent Street
Tel (0926) 425570

This establishment has moved two doors down the street and has exactly reproduced the shop interior in Regency style. Popular with locals, the restaurant has a reputation for good home cooking. Breakfast, coffee, light lunches and afternoon tea are served. Pancakes and strawberry cream sponges are particular favourites. Standard blend, plus Earl Grey and herb tea are offered, served in china crockery.

Pot of tea 50p, set teas £1.75 – £2.75
Open all year, Mon – Sat (except bank holidays), 9am – 5.30pm
Lunches

1 2 3

LEAMINGTON SPA (ROYAL)   Warwickshire   Map 04 SP36

Roosters
37–39 Oxford Street
Tel (0926) 426881

An open plan delicatessen/bistro, the delicatessen offers a fine selection of cheeses from a stock list of 400. The bistro area has an open cold display cabinet and blackboard menu from which to choose. Friendly staff will recommend the popular chocolate brandy cake and apple pie. Light lunches, snacks, afternoon tea and evening meals are served. A choice of speciality teas is available.

Pot of tea 50p, cream tea £1.50
Open all year, Mon – Sat and Sun lunch, 9am – 10pm
Lunch, dinner

LECHLADE   Gloucestershire   Map 03 SO29

Katie's Tearoom and Gift Shop
Marlborough House
High Street
Tel (0367) 52273

This is a small, cosy Cotswold tearoom, to the rear of the gift shop, furnished in cottage style. Morning coffee and afternoon tea are served with homemade teacakes, scones, cakes and pastries, soups and sandwiches, and traditional English puddings and sweets. A choice of tea blends is available served with quality bone china. Smoking is not permitted.

Pot of tea 55p, Cotswold cream tea £1.80
Open all year, every day, 9.30am – 6pm

LEICESTER   Leicestershire   Map 04 SK50

Peacock Alley
62–64 High Street
Tel (0533) 538155

This is a light, spacious 1920s-style establishment with palm trees, pastel décor, circular clothed tables and bentwood chairs. Recently extended, Peacock Alley is now open some evenings. Homemade cakes, gâteaux and scones, savoury pies, hot meals and snacks are served. A choice of 45 tea blends is offered, and tea is well presented in white pots with strainers.

Pot of tea 65p
Open all year, Mon – Sat, 9.15am – 6pm (10pm Wed – Sat)
Lunch, dinner

LEOMINSTER   Hereford and Worcester   Map 03 SO45

The Lower Hundred Craft Workshop
Kimbolton
(just off the A49, north of Leominster)

This converted stone barn now houses a craft workshop, sale room and a pleasant little 'no smoking' tearoom. Homemade cakes, a good cup of tea and friendly service can be enjoyed in pleasant surroundings.

Cup of tea 30p
Open Apr – Oct, daily, 10am – 6pm, Nov daily 10am – 5pm, Dec Sat and Sun 10am – 5pm

---

LEWES   East Sussex   Map 05 TQ41

The Coffee Shop
White Hart Hotel
High Street
Tel (0273) 473794

A small coffee shop is within this historic hotel. The building has Tudor origins and there are beams, wood panelling and low ceilings. Cane armchairs are clustered in fours and there is friendly waitress service. Homemade scones and gâteaux are served with a choice of standard blend or Earl Grey tea.

Set tea £2.50
Open all year, every day, 10am – 10pm
1 2 3

LINCOLN   Lincolnshire   Map 07 SK97

Bishops Table
7 Eastgate Street
Tel (0522) 26442/
511280

This newly opened establishment is part of the Hair, Beauty and Leisure Salon, owned and supervised by Elizabeth Freedman, for use by regular clients and visitors to Lincoln. In the style of the Stuarts, the Bishops Table offers a salad bar, light meals and traditional afternoon teas, carefully presented with bone china.

Pot of tea 55p
Open all year, every day, 10am – 4pm
Light meals
1 3

LINCOLN   Lincolnshire   Map 07 SK97

Whites of Lincoln
The Jews House
15 The Strait
Steep Hill
Tel (0522) 524851

A fine little restaurant which has been continuously occupied as a house for over 800 years – the longest in Europe. It is comfortably furnished with antiques, and because of its size and style children, unfortunately, are not allowed. Lunch is served until 2pm, then afternoon tea with quality flans, scones and teacakes, but the undoubted favourite is the spectacular Charlotte Royale.

Pot of tea 60p, special tea £1.30
Open Feb – Dec, every day high season, 6 days winter, 12noon – 5pm and 7.30pm – 8.45pm
Lunch
1 3

LIVERPOOL   Merseyside   Map 07 SJ39

The Gallery Coffee Shop
Tate Gallery
Albert Dock
Tel 051 – 709 3223 ext 2211

This small self-service coffee shop is situated on the mezzanine floor of the Tate Gallery in the recreated Albert Dock complex. Mostly homemade cakes are served – shortbread, scones, cheesecake, bakewell slice and gâteaux, with sausage rolls and quiche. A choice of tea blends is available and customers can enjoy views of the docks. Smoking is not permitted.

Pot of tea 40p, cakes 50p – 75p
Open all year, Tue – Sun, 11am – 6.45pm

LIVERPOOL   Merseyside   Map 07 SJ39

Waterfront Café
Albert Dock
Tel 051–207 0001

This little café in the former pilotage building forms part of the Merseyside Maritime Museum, which itself is incorporated into the Albert Dock complex with its many activities and areas of interest. Scones and cakes are served, with sandwiches, salads, soup, quiche and baked potatoes. Tea is served in red plastic pots.

Pot of tea 40p, cakes 35p – 85p
Open Easter – Oct, daily (except Christmas, New Year and Good Fri), 10.30am – 5.30pm (last admission 4.30pm) Light meals

---

LLANARMON DYFFRYN CEIRIOG   Clwyd   Map 07 SJ13

Hand Hotel
Tel (069 176) 666

A charming hotel in a lovely setting; tea here is served in the lounge where a welcoming log fire burns in winter or in fine weather one may sit outside. Homemade biscuits, toasted teacakes and scones are available with a choice of tea blends.

Pot of tea 70p, cream tea £1.65
Open mid Mar – Jan, every day, 8am – 10pm
1 2 3

LLANASA   Clwyd   Map 06 SJ18

Llanasa Craft Centre and Restaurant
(Nr. Holywell)
Tel (07456) 4977

This 18th-century H-Plan house stands in a charming Welsh village that has been beautifully renovated and, not surprisingly, has been a winner of the Prince of Wales Award for enterprise and the protection of the environment. The village pond is a haven for wildfowl and beautiful gardens surround the restaurant, where you can enjoy both the array of craft work and a superb afternoon tea, served in fine china. Sandwiches, homemade scones and jam with cream, bara brith and gâteau are all delicious, and the friendly staff make you feel very welcome.

Pot of tea 35–55p, traditional afternoon tea £2.50
Open Easter – Sep every day, 10.30am – 5.30pm Morning coffee and lunches also available
1 2 3

LLANDEILO   Dyfed   Map 02 SN62

Café Royal Patisserie
King Street
Tel (0558) 822908

This small café near the church has polished floorboards, linen covered tables and a cosy atmosphere. A wide choice of tea blends is offered along with éclairs, meringues, gâteaux and pastries. Snacks such as pizzas and pies are also served.

Pot of tea and cake around £1.80 Open all year 8.30am – 5.30pm, daily. Snack meals

---

LLANDEILO   Dyfed   Map 02 SN62

Cawdor Arms Hotel
Tel (0558) 823500

A comfortable Georgian house hotel, the Cawdor
Arms offers a lounge service where one may enjoy tea
with scones, jam and cream in elegant surroundings.

Tea 80p
Open all year, every day
1   3

LLANDEILO   Dyfed   Map 02 SN62

**Trapp Art and Crafts
Centre**
Tel (0269) 850362

Part of the crafts centre, this is a clean, bright, well
maintained tearoom on two floors, with a snack bar
service. Homemade scones, shortbread, bara brith
and gingerbread are served, and there is a choice of
standard blend, Earl Grey or lemon tea.

Pot of tea and scone 80p
Open Nov – Christmas,
Mar – Easter, 11am –
5.30pm, Easter – Oct every
day 11am – 5.30pm (Jul –
Aug to 9pm) Lunches
1   3   &

LLANDOVERY   Dyfed   Map 03 SN73

The Coffee House
High Street

A small café with plastic covered tablecloths and
wheel-back chairs. Homemade cakes, scones, Welsh
cakes and sandwiches are served from a small
counter, and home-cooked hot dishes such as
lasagne, jacket potatoes and ham quiche.

Cup of tea and scone 75p
Open all year

LLANDUDNO   Gwynedd   Map 06 SH78

Habit Tearooms
12 Mustyn Street
Tel (0492) 75043

A green fronted shop on the main street. The
green theme is continued inside with polished pine
tables, high-backed cane chairs, prints and pot plants.
There is a good display of homemade cakes and
scones, and China, Indian, Earl Grey and lemon teas
are served loose leaf in the pot with a strainer.

Pot of tea 40p, cakes 40p –
80p
Open all year, every day,
10am – 5.15pm

LLANDUDNO　Gwynedd　Map 06 SH78

St Tudno Hotel
North Parade
Tel (0492) 74411

The St Tudno is a charming sea-front hotel, run by very hospitable owners who are always on hand to welcome you. The hotel restaurant has a very high reputation for its food and its excellent standards are demonstrated in the delicious scones, meringues, flans and pastries or freshly-made sandwiches. There is a wide choice of tea blends, including some fruit-flavoured teas, which make an interesting change from the normal range. The lounges are beautifully furnished and you can be sure of a comfortable and relaxing atmosphere.

Pot of tea from 85p, sandwiches from £1.50
Open every day except for 3 weeks at Christmas, 7.30am – midnight
⟦1⟧ ⟦2⟧ ⟦3⟧

LLANDUDNO　Gwynedd　Map 06 SH78

Sandbach
78A Mustyn Street
Tel (0492) 76522

A delightful little teashop, situated on the first floor of a charming shop selling handmade chocolates. The pretty teashop is in an area displaying greetings cards, handmade glass and pictures. A selection of cakes, pastries and biscuits is served from the trolley, and there are teacakes and ices. Hot and cold snacks and lunches are available, and a good range of teas.

Pot of tea 50p, Welsh afternoon tea £2
Open all year, Mon – Sat, 9.30am – 5.15pm
Lunch

LLANFAIR PWLLGWYNGYLL　Gwynedd　Map 06 SH57

**James Pringle
Woollen Mill**
Station Site
Tel (0248) 717171

Situated next to the station with the very long name, the teashop is in the large quality-clothing shop. The self-service restaurant is split-level with a tiled floor, polished wooden tables and matching chairs with padded seats. Hot lunches, salads and teas are served, with a good selection of cakes and a choice of six tea blends.

Pot of tea and teacake 95p
Open all year, every day, 9am – 5.30pm (10am – 5.30pm Sun)
Lunch
♿

LLANGEFNI   Gwynedd   Map 06 SH47

The Whole Thing
5 Field Street
Tel (0248) 724832

This bright, fresh little wholefood restaurant and coffee shop is situated over a popular wholefood shop. The décor is simple but pleasant, in a country style, with plain walls and carpets, pine furniture and pictures for sale. A really excellent display of home baking, including flapjacks and carrot cake, is offered, and a choice of teas is available. There is a daily blackboard menu for wholefood, wholesome hot dishes such as lentil, carrot and coriander soup and pasta vegetable bake. Smoking is not permitted.

Open all year, Mon – Fri, 9am – 5.30pm
Lunch

LLANRHAEADR   Clwyd   Map 06 SJ06

The Lodge
Tel (074 578) 370

This former lodge on the main A525 has been converted into an exclusive ladies' clothing shop and teashop. Light lunches and homemade cakes, including brewsoin cake, sponges and cheesecakes, are available and there is also a small dispenser bar. Standard blend, lemon and China tea is served with Hornsea pottery.

Pot of tea 45p
Open all year, Mon – Sat (except bank holidays), 9.30am – 5.30pm summer, 10am – 5pm winter
Light lunches
1 3

LLANRWST   Gwynedd   Map 06 SH76

The Old Tannery
Willow Street
Tel (0492) 640185

Part of an antique shop and kitchen display, old tables, church pews and chairs are situated among antique furniture, clocks and pot plants, creating a pleasant atmosphere enhanced by friendly service. Homemade cakes and scones are served with pizzas, various snacks and sandwiches.

Pot of tea 40p, cakes 45p
Open all year, Mon – Sat, 9am – 4pm
Snack meals
3

LLANTWIT MAJOR   South Glamorgan   Map 03 SS96

Major Café
East Street
Tel (04465) 4922

This small self-service café is a few steps up from the entrance at street level. The menu offers mainly hot meals and snacks, but homemade scones, fancy cakes, apple pie, gâteaux and cheesecake are also served.

Pot of tea 40p
Open all year, Mon – Sat,
9am – 6pm
Lunches

LOCHGILPHEAD   Strathclyde   *Argyllshire*   Map 10 NR88

The Smiddy
Smithy Lane
Tel (0546) 3606

This little gem is tucked away in a lane behind the main shopping area. Once the smithy stables, it is now a popular cottage-style coffee shop and licensed bistro. Only fresh, whole, natural food is served, with vegetarian dishes and seafood featuring strongly. The superb home baking includes florentines, peanut butter slices, and oatmeal toffee cake, but the moist passion cake is particularly recommended. A choice of leaf teas, including herbal, is available. Smoking is not permitted.

Pot of tea 45p – 50p
Open all year, every day summer, Mon – Sat winter
   Summer Mon – Sat
10am – 10pm, Sun noon – 8pm
   Winter Mon – Thu 10am – 5.30pm, Fri – Sat 10am – 10pm
Lunch, dinner
3

LONDON NW3

Holiday Inn
128 King Henry's Road
Swiss Cottage
Tel 01 – 722 7711

A busy, modern, cosmopolitan hotel where tea is served by pleasant, helpful staff in the comfortable lounge. A good selection of gâteaux, cheesecakes and sandwiches is available, and a choice of tea blends is offered.

Pot of tea £1.30, set afternoon tea £6.50
Open all year, every day, 10am – 10.30pm, tea served 3pm – 5pm
   &

LONDON SW1

Hyatt Carlton Tower
Cadogan Place
Tel 01–235 6000

This luxurious, modern, five-star hotel just off Sloane Street is well placed to revive you after shopping either in Knightsbridge or in Chelsea. Afternoon tea is served in its delightful Chinoiserie Lounge, which is famous for its spectacular arrangements of fresh flowers. As a background to the ritual of afternoon tea, harp music plays softly in the afternoons. Speciality teas include some quite unusual ones – China rose petal, Russian caravan, Japan cherry, China black, jasmine, gunpowder, as well as Darjeeling, Earl Grey and mint. Sandwiches, scones and pastries are served by friendly waiters and waitresses.

Set tea £8.50
Open daily 3 – 5.30pm
 1 2 3

LONDON SW1

Hyde Park Hotel
Knightsbridge
Tel 01–235 2000

Views over Hyde Park from the delightful Park Room Restaurant help you to relax over the delicious afternoon teas served in this traditional English hotel, which is a welcome refuge from the hustle and bustle of Knightsbridge. Pastries, scones and gâteaux may be accompanied by a choice of teas – Darjeeling, Assam, Earl Grey, Lapsang Souchong – or infusions, for example, spice, imperial, vanilla, all served in excellent silver and fine china, and there is live music as background entertainment.

Set tea £9
Open every day 4 – 6pm
1 2 3

LONDON SW1

Stafford Hotel
St James's Place
Tel 01 – 493 0111

Sister to the famous Ritz Hotel, and only a few minutes' walk away in St James's, the Stafford is a peaceful haven just off Piccadilly and close to Green Park. Afternoon tea is served in the elegant lounge, and the choice of teas, besides Indian or China, includes mint and various herbal blends. The set afternoon tea begins with a selection of dainty finger sandwiches, followed by toasted scones with jam and cream, and ends with a choice of homemade patisseries. The service is highly professional, which, together with the fine china and luxurious setting, helps to create a soothing atmosphere in which to relax after a busy day.

Full afternoon tea £8
Open daily 3 – 5.30pm
1   2   3

LONDON SW19

Cannizaro House
West Side
Wimbledon Common
Tel 01 – 879 1464

Standing in gardens on the edge of Wimbledon Common, this is a most attractive, historic building, beautifully transformed into a luxurious hotel. The elegant drawing room, with its comfortable chairs, antiques and paintings, is the elegant setting for afternoon teas, with homemade scones, fruit cake, strawberry tartlets, shortbread and a range of excellent patisseries and sandwich triangles. A good choice of tea varieties includes China White Point, jasmine, Assam, Darjeeling, Earl Grey, mango and passion fruit, and they are nicely served in china pots by an efficient staff.

Afternoon teas £5.50 – £8.50
Open all year, every day, 3pm – 5.30pm
1   2   3   ♿

LONDON W1

Britannia Inter-Continental
Grosvenor Square
Tel 01 – 629 9400

A modern comfortable lounge is the setting for afternoon tea in this popular and luxurious hotel overlooking Grosvenor Square. A range of tea blends is available to accompany the selection of sandwiches, homemade scones, cakes and gâteaux.

Afternoon tea £7.50
Open all year, every day, 3pm – 5.30pm

LONDON W1

Browns Hotel
Albermarle and Dover
Streets
Tel 01 – 493 6020

This most English of hotels now spans 12 houses, and preservation orders ensure that their appearance and decorative detail are preserved amid the luxury shops and galleries of Mayfair. Inside, oak panelling and stained glass contribute to the calm and discreet atmosphere. Tea is served in the lounge in 'Hathaway Rose' bone china and you can choose from a wide range of Indian, China and herbal teas. Refreshments, bought by the professional, cheerful staff, comprise sandwiches, brown bread and butter and preserves, toasted, buttered scones with clotted cream, and delectable homemade cakes and pastries.

Set tea £8.95
Open every day 3 – 6pm
1 2 3

LONDON W1

Churchill Hotel
Portman Square
Tel 01 – 486 5800

This modern hotel has a sunken lounge where a harpist entertains and fresh flowers are displayed amid glittering chandeliers. Full afternoon tea is served, comprising finger sandwiches, homemade fruit scone with Devonshire cream and strawberry jam, and assorted pastries. Loose-leaf tea is well served and a choice of blends is offered.

Pot of tea £2, set tea £8.50
(£6 for children under 10 years)
Open all year, every day, 3.30pm – 5.30pm
1 2 3

LONDON W1

Claridges Hotel
Brook Street
Tel 01 – 629 8860

One of London's most famous hotels, Claridges serves its afternoon teas with style, as befits a distinguished hotel, accustomed to catering for the needs of guests who may be members of royal houses, stars of stage and screen, or international business tycoons. The setting for tea is the lounge foyer, which leads off the impressive marbled and pillared entrance hall. Service, by tail-coated staff, is excellent; the tea, whether you take Earl Grey, Assam, Lapsang Souchong or one of the various herbal infusions is fresh and well flavoured, the scones, French pastries and gâteaux are as delicious as one would expect from the chefs here.

Set tea £9
Open every day 4 – 5.15pm
1 2 3

LONDON W1

Cumberland Hotel
Marble Arch
Tel 01–262 1234

The hotel is nicely placed to attract weary Oxford Street shoppers, being close to Marble Arch. Traditional afternoon tea is served in the comfortable lounge, or a coffee shop provides lighter refreshments. Both lounge and coffee shop have table service.

Pot of tea £1, set tea in lounge £7
Open 3pm – 5pm in lounge, 9.30am – 11.30pm in coffee shop
1 2 3

LONDON W1

Grafton Hotel
Tottenham Court Road
Tel 01–388 4131

Conveniently situated at the northern end of Tottenham Court Road, this is a lively hotel, its spacious lounge has comfortable armchairs and sofas and is decorated with numerous pictures. Pleasant waitresses serve a choice of blends of tea with biscuits or accompanying a full afternoon tea of sandwiches, scones and cakes.

Tea and biscuits £1.20, set tea £6.50
Open all year, every day, 3pm – 5pm
1 2 3

LONDON W1

Inn on the Park
Hamilton Terrace, Park Lane
Tel 01–499 0888

Many people would rate this as the best modern hotel in London. The marble-floored entrance hall, with its beautiful fresh flowers and greenery leads you into the foyer lounge where very pleasant and helpful waitresses will take your order for tea as you settle into the comfortable armchairs. There are three different set teas, and a good choice of speciality teas to drink, including gunpowder and Queen Mary's blend. Scones, French pastries and gâteaux are all freshly made and delicious.

Set teas £7.50, £8, £9
Open every day 3 – 6pm
1 2 3 &

LONDON W1

London Hilton
22 Park Avenue
Tel 01–493 8000

Tea is served in the large, airy, modern lounge of this famous international hotel. Tables are well set out and there is a pleasing background of taped music. Crumpets with honey, French pastries and gâteaux are served and a choice of tea blends is offered. As one might expect, tea is beautifully presented in good china.

Set tea £8.50
Open all year, every day, 3 – 6pm

LONDON W1

Marriott Hotel, Regent Lounge
Grosvenor Square
Tel 01–493 1232

This charming hotel lounge overlooking Grosvenor Square is a relatively undiscovered oasis in the heart of Mayfair, and makes an ideal afternoon rendezvous. Full traditional afternoon teas, with sandwiches, scones and cake, or Devonshire cream teas are served in style, or if you prefer, you can have a selection of mouth-watering sandwiches or excellent pastries and gâteaux from the trolley. Specialities like Viennese Sacher Torte or New York cheesecake are hard to resist. Tea is freshly made and nicely served in china teapots by helpful waitresses. There is a choice of five different speciality teas and blends; ice cream and various coffees are also available.

Pot of tea £1.40, pastries and gâteaux £2.50, full afternoon tea £6.75
Open daily 3 – 6pm

LONDON W1

Le Meridien
Piccadilly
Tel 01–734 8000

Owned by Air France, this de luxe, five-star hotel at the very centre of London has all the elegance associated with the interior décor of France, with chandeliers and mirrors everywhere, and spacious rooms with attractive, ornamental ceilings. Various sorts of Indian and China tea are offered, as well as Russian caravan, Kenyan and Ceylon orange pekoe. French pastries and gâteaux are the highlights of afternoon tea here, but there are also traditional English scones and sultana buns.

Set tea £7.75
Open every day

LONDON W1

Park Lane Hotel
Piccadilly
Tel 01 – 499 6321

The Park Lane Hotel offers an excellent selection of herbal teas, China teas – gunpowder, China rose, passion fruit and jasmine – as well as the more usual Ceylon, Assam and Darjeeling. The setting is the Palm Court Lounge, a long-established, popular rendezvous with an elegant 1920s atmosphere, live piano music to entertain the clientèle, and pleasant service. You can have a full afternoon tea, or choose fresh or toasted sandwiches – perhaps a three-layered toasted sandwich of egg, bacon, chicken, tomato, or perhaps mayonnaise and coleslaw. The homemade cakes and pastries are excellent.

Pot of tea £1.75, set tea £7.25, pastries £2.20
Open daily for snacks 10am – 11pm, set afternoon tea 3 – 6pm

1 2 3

LONDON W1

Portman Intercontinental
22 Portman Square
Tel 01 – 486 5844

Comfortable sofas and easy chairs abound in the wood-panelled lounge lobby which is laid out for afternoon tea every day. Service is attentive and very efficient under the eye of the lounge manager, who ensures that everyone's needs are met. For tea choose either the Portman's own blend, Indian, Ceylon, China or Earl Grey, brought to you freshly made and well flavoured in a silver teapot. The set afternoon tea consists of a selection of sandwiches, followed by freshly-baked scones and patisseries. Portman Square is just north of Oxford Street, and tea here makes an ideal finish to a day's shopping.

Set afternoon tea £7
Open daily 3.30 – 5.30pm

1 2 3

LONDON W1

Ritz Hotel
Piccadilly
Tel 01 – 493 8181

No other English hotel has such strong associations with afternoon tea as the Ritz, where the Palm Court Lounge is a byword for elegance and preserves an Edwardian atmosphere, with its pink-cupped chandeliers, rose-coloured Louis XVI chairs and marble tables. The Palm Court is very popular at tea time, so intending visitors are advised to book a table for either the first or second sitting. Service, under the supervision of an excellent maître d'hôtel, is very friendly, and the dainty sandwiches – cucumber, egg and cress, smoked salmon are traditional favourites – scones and delicious, light, creamy pastries and gâteaux – are all freshly and expertly made every day. Tea at the Ritz is a unique experience.

Set tea £10.50
Open every day, first sitting 3pm; second sitting 4.30pm

LONDON W1

The Selfridge
Orchard Street
Tel 01 – 408 2080

The Selfridge Hotel simply could not be more conveniently placed to receive shoppers from the famous department store, being positioned just off Oxford Street and to the rear of the shop. Tea is served in the fine, panelled first-floor lounge which has comfortable seating around small tables. Service, by uniformed, tail-coated staff, is quiet and efficient. The set tea comprises sandwiches, scones, pastries and gâteaux. All are fresh and excellent, as is the choice of Earl Grey, Assam, Darjeeling and China teas on offer.

Pot of tea £1.60, set tea £7.95
Open all year, every day, 3 – 5.30pm

LONDON W1

Westbury Hotel
Conduit Street
Tel 01 – 629 7755

The Westbury Hotel is an attractive haven just off New Bond Street, at the centre of the West End shopping belt. Tea is served in a particularly pleasant, panelled lounge by staff who look after guests extremely well. Finger sandwiches, scones and pastries are accompanied by a choice of teas which includes Keemun, mint, Darjeeling, Indian and Earl Grey. The pretty, high-quality china adds to the enjoyment of the occasion.

Set tea £8.50
Open every day, 3 – 6pm

LONDON W2

Royal Lancaster Hotel
Lancaster Terrace
Tel 01 – 262 6737

This is a large, modern hotel in Bayswater, with a cosmopolitan atmosphere and views over Hyde Park. There is a pleasant, first-floor lounge where afternoon tea is served by friendly and efficient staff who ensure that guests feel welcome. The set tea consists of finger sandwiches, scones and a selection of French pastries, accompanied by Indian, China and Earl Grey tea with milk or lemon served in a china teapot. To help you relax while you enjoy the refreshments a pianist entertains throughout the afternoon.

Set tea £6.25
Open every day, 3 – 5.30pm

LONDON W8

**Kensington Close
Hotel**
Wright's Lane
Tel 01–937 8170

This large, busy hotel is located close to Kensington High Street and tube station. Tea is served in a modern restaurant with a small lounge area. Finger sandwiches, scones and cream, pastries and gâteaux are available with Assam, Darjeeling and Earl Grey teas.

Pot of tea 95p, set tea
£3.75
Open all year, every day, 3 – 5pm

LONDON W8

**Kensington Park
Hotel**
De Vere Gardens
Tel 01–937 8080

Recently opened, the Kensington Park Hotel stands in a quiet street not far from the Albert Hall. Elegant and comfortable surroundings make afternoon tea here a pleasant experience, and for a central London hotel the set tea is very good value. You can choose from several different blends of tea, and there are sandwiches, fruit loaf, freshly baked scones, and assorted pastries and gâteaux over which to relax with your friends after shopping or before the theatre.

Set afternoon tea £4.95
Open every day

LONDON WC1

Hotel Russell
Russell Square
Tel 01–837 6470

At the Russell, tea is served in the comfortable hotel lounge, with formal waiter service. Afternoon tea comprises homemade scones, cakes, sandwiches and China or Indian tea.

Pot of tea £1.25, set tea
£6.50
Open all year, every day, 3 – 5.30pm

LONDON WC2

Savoy Hotel
Strand
Tel 01–836 4343

Afternoon tea at the Savoy, one of London's most famous hotels, could not be other than a memorable experience. The surroundings are sumptuous, and the ornate Thames Foyer, with its central gazebo is an evocative setting in which to enjoy this most traditional of English institutions. Service of the blend of tea of your choice, accompanied by excellent sandwiches, scones and pastries, is very much in the grand manner, with the tail-coated staff taking pride in making the occasion something special. If you have a taste for luxury, this is definitely the place to choose.

Set afternoon tea £9.25
Open daily, 3.30 – 5.30pm
1 2 3

LONDON WC2

Waldorf Hotel
The Aldwych
Tel 01–836 2400

On Friday, Saturday and Sunday 'You never know who *you* might meet at a Waldorf Afternoon Tea Dance', as the hotel's brochure invites you to discover. The Waldorf's delightful Palm Court is the setting for the revival of this fashionable pre-war entertainment, at which each course is served at a relaxed pace to allow plenty of intervals for dancing. On other days of the week a lavish afternoon tea is offered, without the dancing but with a pianist. Waldorf teas feature toasted English muffins, as well as sandwiches, bridge rolls, scones with clotted cream, fresh pastries or gâteaux, accompanied by a choice of blends of tea, all served with a courtesy that matches the surroundings and takes you back to an age of leisure.

Set afternoon tea £8.95
Afternoon tea dance
£13.75
Open Mon – Thu for tea,
Fri – Sun for afternoon tea
dance 3.30 – 6.30pm
1 2 3

Cadbury's Chocolate Biscuits

Cadbury's Chocolate Biscuits
make the perfect snack, whatever the occasion...
Out and about, Watching T.V.,
Lunch Boxes,
Parties

BRITAIN

At Your Leisure

This is a book to help the active over-50s with time on their hands to get the best out of the 'happiest days of their lives'.

It is a unique touring guide, allowing all members of the family to enjoy some of the more delightful and unusual places in Britain, at their own pace and in their own time – perhaps out of season or midweek. Important information is included on ease of access and difficult terrain.

There is also expert advice on subjects such as health, finance, holidays, making new friends and if (or when) to move house.

MAKING THE GOING EASY AT MORE THAN 500 SELECTED PLACES TO VISIT

LONGHORSLEY   Northumberland   Map 12 NZ19

Linden Hall Hotel
Tel (0670) 516611

This fine country mansion retains much of the grandeur of bygone days. Tea is served in the elegant, high-ceilinged drawing room which leads off an impressive galleried and domed hall. Amid the grandeur, service is friendly and in the traditional style, at tables covered with linen tablecloths, with cakes borne in on a tiered cake stand. The full afternoon tea consists of sandwiches (cucumber, smoked salmon, egg), scones with cream and jam, cakes and biscuits, all homemade and very enjoyable. Assam, Earl Grey, Ceylon, Darjeeling or peppermint infusion are the choices of teas.

Linden tea (scones, cakes, biscuits) £2.25, full afternoon tea £3.75
Open every day 4 – 5.30pm
$\boxed{1}$ $\boxed{2}$ $\boxed{3}$

LONG MELFORD   Suffolk   Map 05 TL84

The Gladstone Tearooms
4 Westgate Street
Tel (0787) 881544

This friendly teashop is situated in a small row of antique shops and houses just outside the town. Attractively decorated in floral prints, with clothed tables and fresh flowers, there is a display cabinet with a selection of appetising homebaked cakes. Darjeeling, Earl Grey and Assam teas are available. Smoking is not permitted.

Pot of tea 70p, cream tea £1.80
Open all year, Tue – Sun, 10am – 6pm

LOUTH   Lincolnshire   Map 08 TF38

Crusty's ·
Pawn Shop Passage

A small, modern café, Crusty's provides friendly table service. Toasted crumpets, muffins and teacakes are available with a range of homemade cakes. Full afternoon tea includes fresh sandwiches, and substantial hot snacks are also served throughout the day. A choice of tea blends is offered. Smoking is not permitted.

Pot of tea 50p, full afternoon tea £2.15
Open all year, Tue – Sat, 10am – 4pm (Thu 10am – 2pm)
Hot snacks

LUDLOW   Shropshire   Map 07 SO57

Hardwicks
2 Quality Square
Tel (0584) 6470

In pleasant split-level ground floor premises, Hardwicks has white cottage style furniture, and is tucked away in a small cobbled square off the High street. As well as homemade scones and cakes, light cooked meals are served, including vegetarian dishes. Indian, China and herb teas are served in china teapots with matching crockery.

Pot of tea 50p
Open all year, Mon – Sat, 10am – 5pm

LULWORTH   Dorset   Map 03 SY88

Old Boathouse Café
Tel (092 941) 648

This small seafront café which has been modernised with banquet seating, formica tables and bright décor. The self-service counter displays a good range of homemade scones, cakes, pies and sandwiches. Hot snacks and dairy ice cream are available.

Cream tea £1.60
Open Easter – Oct, every day, 10am – 6pm
Snack meals

LUSTLEIGH   Devon   Map 03 SX78

Eastwrey Barton Hotel and Restaurant
Moretonhampstead Road
Tel (06477) 338

Set amid acres of woodland in the beautiful Wrey Valley on the southern edge of Dartmoor National Park is this small, hospitable country-house hotel. There is a cosy lounge and restaurant and in warm weather one may sit in the garden. Homemade pastries, scones and fruitcake are available, with a selection of tea blends served in the traditional way.

Cream tea around £2.50
Open all year, every day, 3pm – 5.30pm
1 3

LYMINGTON   Hampshire   Map 04 SZ39

The Buttery
19 High Street
Tel (0590) 72870

A 15th-century teashop, the Buttery is simply appointed with formica tables, and self-service and table service sections. There is a good variety of home baking, including cheese scones, flapjacks and chocolate caramel shortbread. A range of tea blends is offered, served in china pots.

Teas £1.95 – £2.20
Open all year, every day Easter – Sep, closed Sun in winter, 8.15am – 5.15pm self-service, 10am – 4.45pm table service

---

LYMINGTON   Hampshire   Map 04 SZ39

Lentune Coffee House
4 Quay Street
Tel (0590) 72766

This charming beamed 16th-century cottage is set between the Quay and the High Street, with simple appointments and fresh flowers. Snack meals and a good selection of homemade cakes are offered, such as coffee gâteau, fruitcake, shortbread, almond slice and gingerbread. Earl Grey, lemon and herb tea are offered, as well as the popular blend.

Pot of tea 50p, cream tea £2, farmhouse tea £1.75
Open Mar – Nov, Wed – Mon, 10am – 5pm

LYMINGTON   Hampshire   Map 04 SZ39

Passford House Hotel
Mount Pleasant Lane
Tel (0590) 682398

Relax in comfort with a choice of lounges, one with a log fire when it is chilly. Order Indian or China tea from the porter and help yourself to a selection from the trolley. A variety of sandwiches and scones with jam and cream are always available, with a choice of two other items such as homemade fruit or madeira cake, shortbread or fruit cream tartlet.

Sandwiches £1.50, cakes 50p – £1
Open all year, every day, 3.30pm – 5.30pm

LYNDHURST   Hampshire   Map 04 SU30

Court House Tearooms 97 High Street Tel (042128) 3871	These small, single-storey tearooms are on the Southampton side of Lyndhurst in a built-up area. There is a homely, relaxed atmosphere, with simple furnishings. Homemade white or wholemeal scones, rich fruit cake, date and walnut, apple and almond and chocolate cakes are served, with a choice of tea varieties. Sandwiches, filled rolls and jacket potatoes are also available.	Set teas £1.60 – £1.65 Open all year (except Christmas week), every day, 10.30am – 5.30pm (weekends 6pm, winter 5pm)

LYNDHURST   Hampshire   Map 04 SU30

Crown Hotel High Street Tel (042128) 2922	Tea and country-style biscuits are available in the comfortable lounge, or outside on the terrace on a sunny day, at this elegant hotel. Earl Grey and English breakfast teas are served by uniformed staff.	Pot of tea and biscuits 75p Open all year, every day, any time [1] [2] [3]

LYNDHURST   Hampshire   Map 04 SU30

The Honey Pot Honeysuckle Cottage Restaurant Minstead Tel (0703) 813122	The Honey Pot is a modern annexe building in the garden of the Honeysuckle Cottage Restaurant, an idyllic thatched New Forest Cottage. There are polished tables and Windsor chairs, and tables in the garden for sunny days. Home baking is served with a choice of Earl Grey, Darjeeling or standard blend teas in a china pot with hot water jug.	Queen Bee Tea £2.50, Beehive Tea £2.20, Drones Tea £1.60 Open Easter – Sep, every day, 10.30am – 5.30pm (Oct – Easter weekends only) [1] [3]

LYNDHURST   Hampshire   Map 04 SU30

The Pony Tearoom 21 High Street Tel (042128) 2789	On a busy corner by the traffic lights, this is a simply-furnished teashop with wooden chairs and attractive tablecloths. Lemon meringue pie, rich chocolate gâteau, coffee and walnut cake and apricot and pineapple cheesecake are served.	Pot of tea 45p Open all year, every day, 10.30am – 5pm (3pm – 5pm Sun)

LYTHAM ST ANNES   Lancashire   Map 07 SD32

Serendipity Bedford Hotel 307–311 Clifton Drive South Tel (0253) 724636	A glass-fronted coffee and teashop at the front of the hotel, Serendipity has polished inlaid wood tables and very comfortable chairs – rather quaint in style. Light lunches are available and there is a good salad bar. Tea is served in an elegant silver pot with matching water jug, and homemade cakes are displayed on a three-tier stand. Smoking is not permitted.	Set tea £3.25 Open all year, every day, 10am – 5pm Lunch [1] [3]

MACHYNLLETH　　Powys　　Map 06 SH70

Felin Crewi
Penegoes
Tel (0654) 3113

Part of the working watermill complex, which includes a craft sales area, this tearoom serves granary-type cakes, scones and a good cup of tea. There are ponies and goats outside, as well as ducks on the river.

Cream tea £1.75
High season opening
times 10.30am – 5pm

MACHYNLLETH　　Powys　　Map 06 SH70

National Milk Bar
17–19 Penrallt Street
Tel (0654) 2787

This purpose-built, modern milk bar situated near the famous town clock serves scones and pastries, along with a good cup of tea.

Tea 35p
Open all year, daily,
8.30am – 6pm
Snacks, hot meals

MALMESBURY　　Wiltshire　　Map 03 ST98

The Old Bell Hotel
Tel (0666) 822344

This delightful gabled hotel, next to the abbey, has a claim to be the country's oldest hotel, and retains many interesting features, including a 700-year-old fireplace. In the summer tea is served in the gardens, in the winter in the Garden Lounge or in the bar. The hotel's kitchen produces wonderful scones, cheese scones, cream cakes and gâteaux. The traditional afternoon tea starts with a round of sandwiches, then scones, cream and jam, followed by an éclair or slice of fruitcake, accompanied by Indian or China tea, Lapsang or Earl Grey.

Cream tea £1.95,
traditional afternoon tea
£3.25, pot of tea £1,
toasted teacake £1.
Open every day 3.30 –
5.30pm

MALVERN　　Hereford and Worcester　　Map 03 SO74

Café el Sol
Mount Pleasant Hotel
Belle Vue Terrace
Tel (06845) 61837

This elegant Victorian-style coffee lounge, adjoining the Mount Pleasant Hotel, serves a good selection of breads, cakes, pastries and gâteaux – some homemade, along with eight different blends of tea. Service is friendly and efficient.

Tea 60p per person, 95p
for two
Open all year, Tue – Sun,
10am – 5 pm
Snacks

MALVERN   Hereford and Worcester   Map 03 SO74

Royal Malvern Hotel
Graham Road
Tel (0684) 563411

Pleasant and efficient staff serve afternoon tea in the foyer-lounge of this town-centre hotel. A selection of sandwiches, scones and biscuits is available, along with a traditional pot of tea.

Pot of tea 75p
Open all year, daily
(except Christmas Day), 3
– 6pm
1 2 3

MANCHESTER   Greater Manchester   Map 07 SJ89

Holiday Inn Crown Plaza
Peter Street
Tel 061 – 236 3333

The elegant Terrace Lounge of this distinctive Edwardian hotel in the town centre offers an attractive setting for traditional afternoon tea. Home-baked cheesecakes, flans, cakes, pastries and sandwiches can be accompanied by one of the range of teas which includes China, Indian, flower and jasmin.

Set teas £3.95 and £5.95,
pot of tea £1.25
Open all year, daily, 10am
– 5.30pm, afternoon tea
served from 3pm
1 2 3

MANCHESTER   Greater Manchester   Map 07 SJ89

Hotel Piccadilly
Piccadilly Plaza
Tel 061 – 236 8414

Afternoon tea is served in the Garden Rooms lounge at this large town centre hotel. Cakes, gâteaux, fruit tarts, scones and Danish pastries are all home-baked and the tea is properly made.

Pot of tea £1, cakes from
£1.60
Open all year, every day,
all afternoon
1 2 &

MANCHESTER   Greater Manchester   Map 07 SJ89

Portland Thistle Hotel
Portland Street
Piccadilly Gardens
Tel 061 – 228 3400

Situated on Piccadilly Gardens in the city centre, this hotel serves afternoon teas in its compact, but comfortable lounges. Home-baked scones, gâteaux and pastries are accompanied by a fresh pot of tea.

Pot of tea and scone £1.60
Open all year, every day,
2.30 – 5.30pm
1 2 3

MANCHESTER   Greater Manchester   Map 07 SJ89

Ramada Renaissance Hotel
Blackfriars Street
Tel 061 – 835 2555

Afternoon tea is served in the Fairbairns Lounge on the mezzanine floor of this large modern city-centre hotel. The home-baked selection includes scones, Danish pastries, fruitcake, tartlets and chocolate éclairs and the tea – there is a good choice of blends – is served in attractive china.

Set tea £3.50, pot of tea
£1.50
Open all year, daily,
10.30am – 11pm,
afternoon tea 2.30 – 11pm
Morning coffee, snacks

MARKET HARBOROUGH   Leicestershire   Map 04 SP78

Café Genevieve
53 High Street
Tel (0858) 410257

Tucked away behind the Genevieve dress shop, this pretty little café provides a choice of gâteaux, cakes, scones, teacakes and waffles and freshly made tea – a simple, shoppers' café with friendly staff.

Pot of tea from 55p
Open all year, Tue – Sat
10am – 5pm, Sun 12 noon
– 5.30 pm
Lunches, vegetarian dishes

MARLBOROUGH   Wiltshire   Map 04 SU16

The Polly Tea Rooms
Tel (0672) 52146

The bow windows, low-beamed ceilings and flowered tablecloths of the Polly Tea Rooms create the right background for the stunning range of homemade cakes, gâteaux and speciality ice creams, drawing in crowds of people – especially pupils from Marlborough College. Only set teas or ice creams are served. The Polly Tea gives you plain or muesli scones with cream, and a choice of preserves. The Special Gâteau Tea allows you either one generous portion of a luscious creamy gâteau (for example brandy butter, berry yoghurt, Kiwi fruit) or three of the cakes from the day's enormous selection. Delectable ice creams include Dusty Road – coffee and chocolate ice cream with butterscotch sauce, flaked chocolate and whipped cream. There is a choice of blends of tea.

Set teas (or ice creams)
£2.50
Open every day, Mon – Fri
8.30am – 6pm, Sat 8am –
7pm, Sun 9am – 7pm
Breakfast, opening time –
11.30am; Lunch 12 – 3pm
Credit cards accepted for
bills over £5

MARLBOROUGH   Wiltshire   Map 04 5416

The Tudor Tea Rooms
115 High Street
Tel (0672) 52853/
52904

These pretty tearooms are on two floors. Friendly waitresses serve freshly-made tea (choice of Indian, Earl Grey, Lapsang, Darjeeling or decaffeinated) in attractive china teapots, with delicious homemade scones or traditional home-baked cakes, such as Victoria, coffee or chocolate sandwich. Fresh cream cakes, or four different sorts of shortcake, doughnuts, Danish pastries and ice-cream dishes complete the extensive tea menu.

Pot of tea 65p, cream tea
£2.80
Open daily, 9am – 8pm
(except Christmas and
New Year)
Breakfast, lunch and
evening meals also served

MARLOW   Buckinghamshire   Map 04 SU88

**Compleat Angler
Hotel**
Marlow Bridge
Tel (06284) 4444

An afternoon tea at this delightful Thames-side hotel, set on a picturesque curve of the river, gives you the additional pleasure of uninterrupted river views. The hotel takes its name from the famous book by Izaak Walton, written here in 1653. Nowadays, however, the scene is more of pleasure boats than solitary fishermen. On fine summer days you can enjoy the luxuriant, fragrant gardens all around the hotel as you sample the sandwiches, scones and pastries, beautifully served with the accompaniment of India, China, Earl Grey and Darjeeling teas.

Set tea weekdays £7, weekends £7.50
Open every day, 3.30 – 5.30pm
1 2 3

MATLOCK   Derbyshire   Map 08 SK36

Lea Gardens
Lea
Tel (0629) 534380

This small teashop at the entrance to the famous rhododendron gardens is proving to be a popular addition to the centre's amenities. Mrs Tye bakes the cakes and family and friends help in the conservatory-style 'no-smoking' tearoom that extends outside when the weather permits.

Pot of tea 40p, cakes from 35p
Open Easter – mid Jul daily 10am – 5.30pm

MELMERBY   Cumbria   Map 12 NY63

The Village Bakery
(10 miles east of Penrith on A686)
Tel (076881) 515

Converted farm buildings house this family-owned bakery and tearoom/restaurant. Flagstones, natural stonework and exposed beams preserve the rural character, and the emphasis is on organic produce and local stoneground flour. Baking is done on the premises, so everything is fresh. Typical of the mouthwatering specialities are scones with Cumberland rum butter, Parkin, Westmorland spice cake, Grasmere Gingerbread, Borrowdale tea bread and much, much more. The choice of tea blends includes Ceylon, Darjeeling, Earl Grey and Keemun, and there are also herbal and fruit-flavoured teas. In the upstairs gallery is displayed a selection of high-quality craftware, and there is also a conservatory.

Pot of tea from 50p, cream tea £3.25, cakes from about 45p – £1.00 Open all year. Christmas – Easter, Mon – Sat, mornings only. Easter – Christmas, every day (except Mon pm unless it's a bank holiday), Mon 8.30am – 12.30pm, Tue – Sat 8.30am – 5pm, Sun 9.30am – 5pm
No Smoking
Breakfast, lunch and snacks also served

MICKLETON   Gloucestershire   Map 04 SP14

Three Ways Hotel
Tel (0386) 438429

Afternoon tea has been a popular feature of the Three Ways for some time. Guests can relax in the extensive lounges and there is plenty of outside seating. Home-baked scones, sponges and biscuits accompany a choice of teas and herbal infusions.

Cream tea £1.65
Open all year, daily,
7.30am (8am Sun) – 9pm
(9.30pm Fri and Sat)
☐1☐ ☐2☐ ☐3☐ ☐&☐

MILFORD HAVEN   Dyfed   Map 02 SM90

Rabaiotti's Café and Restaurant
31 Charles Street
Tel (06462) 2576

This large, self-service café offers a varied selection of home-baked cakes, pastries, sandwiches and hot snacks and a good pot of tea. The restaurant has waitress service.

Pot of tea and two Welsh cakes 98p
Open all year, Mon – Sat,
9am – 6.30pm
Lunch and dinner in restaurant

MOFFAT   Dumfries and Galloway   *Dumfriesshire*   Map 11 NT00

Fountain Coffee Shop
65–67 High Street
Tel (0683) 20938

This pleasant, clean and freshly decorated teashop in the centre of town is personally run by the owners, Mr and Mrs Leggate. The biscuits, cakes, scones and shortbread are homemade, and the tea is served by the cup or pot, with a choice of blends.

Tea 50p
Open all year, daily, 10am – 5pm

MONIFIETH   Tayside   *Angus*   Map 12 NO53

Brookside Coffee House
12 Brook Street
Tel (0382) 535040

This quaint little family-run coffee room and ice cream parlour is tucked away in a quiet residential road behind the main shopping street. Most of the baking is homemade – cheesecake, banana loaf and hot cloutie dumpling with fresh cream – and the choice of tea ranges from 'everyday' to fruit and herbal blends.

Set afternoon tea 80p, pot of tea 35p
Open all year, Tue – Sun, summer 10am – 6pm, winter 10am – 4.30pm
Morning coffee, snacks, ice cream specialities

MORECAMBE   Lancashire   Map 07 SD46

Tradewinds
Strathmore Hotel
East Promenade
Tel (0524) 421234

Traditional afternoon tea of home-baked scones, cream, preserve, cake, assorted sandwiches and a fresh pot of tea is served by friendly staff in the lounge of this seafront hotel.

Set tea £3
Open all day, tea served 2 – 6pm
☐1☐ ☐2☐ ☐3☐ ☐&☐

MORETON-IN-MARSH   Gloucestershire   Map 04 SP23

**Cotswold
Restaurant,
Coffeehouse and
Patisserie**
High Street
Tel (0608) 50365

This busy high street teashop and patisserie is wood-panelled with polished tables and chairs. Mr Kay and his staff provide attentive service along with homemade cakes, sandwiches and a traditional cup of tea. This is a 'no smoking' establishment.

Tea 50p, speciality tea 75p, set tea £1.85
Open Apr – Dec, Thu – Tue, 9.30am – 4pm/6pm Lunch

MORETON-IN-MARSH   Gloucestershire   Map 04 SP23

**Marshmallow
Tearooms**
High Street
Tel (0608) 51536

Access to this tearoom is through a small souvenir shop. Once inside, Lynn and Tony Mortibay and their small team serve homemade cakes and sweets, including chocolate fudge cake with ice cream and toasted waffles with maple syrup, and nine different blends of tea. The patio garden is popular during the warmer months.

Pot of tea 45p, speciality tea 65p, set tea £1.95
Open all year, daily, 9am – 5pm
Light lunches
1 2 3

MOULSFORD-ON-THAMES   Oxfordshire   Map 04 SU85

**Beetle and Wedge
Hotel**
Ferry Lane
Tel (0491) 651381 and 651376

This is a delightful riverside hotel with gardens. Afternoon tea can be taken on the terrace or, in colder months, in the cosy lounge. The scones, pastries, cakes and muffins are homemade and the tea is beautifully served in china teapots with a choice of blends.

Full cream tea £7.50
Open all year, daily, 3.30 – 5.30pm
1 2 3

MUCH WENLOCK   Shropshire   Map 07 SO69

The Malthouse
44 High Street
Tel (0952) 727467

This delightful old Shropshire town with its lovely ruined Abbey attracts many visitors who find this first-floor café above a craft shop a welcome place for tea. Scones, teacakes and cakes are all home-made, and there is a choice of Indian, or Earl Grey tea and herbal infusions.

Pot of tea 55p, set teas £1.25 – £2.75
Open all year, Wed – Sun, 3 – 5pm (5.30pm at weekends)
Light meals also served

MUDEFORD   Dorset   Map 04 SZ19

**Waterford Lodge
Hotel**
87 Bure Lane
Friars Cliff
Tel (0425) 272948

Traditional afternoon tea is served by friendly and attentive staff in the lounge of this attractive hotel.

Set tea £2.80
Open all year, every day, teas served 3 – 5.30pm
1 2 3

NAIRN   Highland   *Nairnshire*   Map 14 NH85

Culloden Pottery Restaurant
The Old Smiddy
Gollanfield, Culloden
Tel (0667) 62749

On the first floor, above a gift shop and an established studio pottery, this restaurant specialises in freshly-prepared wholefood cooking. There is a chair lift for the elderly and disabled. Homemade scones, cakes and biscuits are available, as well as a choice of tea blends. There are very pleasant views of the Moray Firth and the surrounding countryside.

Pot of tea 40p
Open all year, every day (but closed between Christmas and New Year), 10am – 5.30pm (later in summer)
Meals and snacks served

NANTWICH   Cheshire   Map 07 SJ65

Chatwin's Coffee Lounge
The Square
Tel (0270) 625688

This self-service first-floor coffee lounge is above a bakery/confectioners opposite the church in the pedestrianised centre of this historic and picturesque old town. There is a variety of freshly-made cakes and Continental patisserie, and a choice of Ceylon, Darjeeling or Earl Grey teas is available.

Tea about 40p, coffee 46p, cream cakes 60p
Open all year, Mon – Sat, 9.30am – 4.30pm
Light meals available

NANTWICH   Cheshire   Map 07 SJ65

Piecemeal
76 Beam Street
Tel (0270) 624997

This canopied street-level restaurant in the town centre features cakes and cream teas, as well as light meals, a children's menu, and a Welsh rarebit special. All the food at Piecemeal is homemade.

Tea about 75p
Open all year, Mon – Sat, 9am – 5pm
Light lunches served

NETHYBRIDGE   Highland   *Inverness-shire*   Map 14 NJ02

Pollyanna's
Tigh-na-Fraoch
Tel (047982) 342

This craft and teashop sells quality goods and gifts and local paintings, as well as speciality teas, herbal infusions and preserves. There is a good selection of cakes, including sultana scones, oat squares, florentines and 'millionaires shortbread'. The comprehensive choice of teas includes Assam, Ceylon, Darjeeling, Earl Grey and jasmine, as well as fruit-flavoured teas and herbal infusions. Although small, this really is a delightfull place – well worth a visit. No smoking is permitted.

Afternoon tea £1.55
Open mid Feb – mid Oct, Tue – Sun, 9.30am (10.30am Sun) – 5pm (4pm Thu)

NEWARK-ON-TRENT　Nottinghamshire　Map 08 SK75

Ponds
7/9 Millgate
Tel (0636) 74822

Set just off the main street, this old teashop, with its low-beamed ceiling and brick floors dates back to 1740. The décor is fresh and bright, with marble-topped tables, fresh flowers and pot plants. Delicious homemade cakes, scones, crêpes and snacks are served, as well as a choice of very good-flavoured tea blends served in crockery pots. 'Excellent', according to our inspector.

Teas about £1
Open all year, Tue – Sun,
10.30am – 5pm
Lunches served, dinners
served Thu – Sat, 7 –
10.30pm

NEWBURY　Berkshire　Map 04 SU46

Café Nouveau
22 The Mall
Tel (0635) 521122

Located in the central mall of Newbury's new covered Kennet shopping centre, this is a pleasant, bustling place for tea. A good variety of English and French pastries, breads and snacks are available, and a tasty cup of tea is served by friendly staff.

Tea about 35p
Open all year, Mon – Sat,
8am – 5.30pm
Snacks available

NEWBURY　Berkshire　Map 04 SU46

Crafty Cat
5 Inch's Yard
Tel (0635) 35491

Pine tables and chairs and a fresh décor welcomes visitors to this well-run coffee house. A nice choice of cake includes carrot cake, banana cake and caramel squares, and there is quite a wide choice of teas and herbal infusions. The staff provide efficient, friendly service.

Pot of tea 60p, cream tea
£1.75
Open all year, Mon – Sat,
8am – 5pm (closes 10pm
Tues – Sat)
Meals served

NEWBURY　Berkshire　Map 04 SU46

**Penthouse
Restaurant, Camp
Hopson**
Northbrook Street
Tel (0635) 523523

Located at the back of the first floor in this department store, this modern tearoom is simply furnished, with a tempting array of cakes and a sweet trolley. Scones, meringues and cheesecake are among the items available, as well as a choice of tea blends.

Pot of tea 50p, afternoon
tea £2
Open all year, Mon – Sat
9.45am – 5.45pm

NEWCASTLE-UPON-TYNE   Tyne and Wear   Map 12 NZ26

Fenwick's Tearooms
Fenwick's Department Store
39 Northumberland Street
Tel 091–232 5100

This lively and popular department store has three café areas, some self-service, others with table service. All the food is made on the premises and there is a good choice of sandwiches, scones and pastries, and blends of tea. Staff are both friendly and efficient.

Pot of tea 40 – 45p, cakes from 58p, set teas £1.50 – £2.55
Open all year except bank holidays, Mon – Sat 9am – 5.30 pm (Thu, 8pm)

NEWCASTLE-UPON-TYNE   Tyne and Wear   Map 12 NZ26

Next 'Brasserie'
15/19 Northumberland Street
Tel 091–232 0226 ext 134

This large popular in-store brasserie is styled on the theme of a 50s/60s milk bar. The self-service choices include a good range of baking, with the emphasis on wholefoods, vegetarian and healthy eating. There is a choice of tea blends, as well as a variety of other drinks – different coffees, hot chocolate and milkshakes.

Pot of tea 60p, afternoon tea £1.65
Open all year, Mon – Sat, 9.30am – 5pm (5.30pm Sat)
Light snacks available
1 2 3

NEW GALLOWAY   Dumfries and Galloway   *Kirkcudbrightshire*   Map 11 NX67

The Smithy
High Street
Tel (06442) 269

This converted blacksmith's shop houses a craft and book shop and a tourist information centre, as well as a pleasant tearoom and restaurant. A range of homemade scones, shortbread, cakes and pies, as well as a menu of snacks and light meals, are available all day.

Pot of tea 35p
Open Mar – Oct, every day, 10am – 6pm (until 9pm Easter – Oct)
Lunches and snacks served

NEW MILTON   Hampshire   Map 04 SZ29

Chewton Glen Hotel
Tel (0425) 275341

Well-kept gardens surround this beautiful and luxurious New Forest hotel, a house associated with the Victorian author Captain Marryat, who wrote *Children of the New Forest*, his much-loved children's story, here. Afternoon tea is an elegant occasion consisting of delicate sandwiches, homemade scones with clotted cream and preserves, and a selection of tempting homemade pastries. The choice of speciality teas includes Keemun, China Oolong, Rose Pouchong, jasmine, gunpowder, Darjeeling, Earl Grey, Lapsang Souchong, traditional English, or herbal infusions.

Traditional afternoon tea £7, with strawberries and cream (in season) £9
Open all year, every day, 3.30pm – 6pm
1 2 3

NEWTONMORE   Highland   *Inverness-shire*   Map 14 NN79

The Tea Cosy
Main Street
Tel (05403) 315

This small teashop is part of a book and craft shop. It only seats 11 people, but it is well worth waiting for a table, browsing among the books and crafts while you do so, because Anne Bertram's country baking is a treat it would be a pity to miss. Shortbreads, scones, ginger biscuits, sponge and fruitcakes, coffee and walnut cake, lemon whisky cake, banana bread and homemade jams present a stunning choice. The good range of teas includes Blue Lady and several fruit-flavoured teas (mango and strawberry, lemon, passion fruit). Smoking is not permitted inside, but weather permitting, there is one table out-of-doors.

Afternoon tea £2.75, pot of tea (for one) 38p – 44p, scone and jam 45p
Open Easter – Oct 10am – 5pm

NEWTON STEWART   Dumfries and Galloway *Wigtownshire*   Map 10 NX46

The Chatterbox
73 Victoria Street
Tel (0671) 3967

This small high-street tea and coffee shop has a fresh décor, with pretty tablecloths and upholstered chairs. Friendly and efficient staff offer a good selection of homemade scones, tea breads, cakes and biscuits, as well as a choice of several tea blends – all well-flavoured and freshly made.

Pot of tea 50p
Open all year, Mon – Sat, 10am – 4.30pm

NORTHALLERTON   North Yorkshire   Map 08 SE39

Betty's Café Tea Rooms
188 High Street
Tel (0609) 775154

This café is part of a small group of establishments based in Harrogate (see entries under Harrogate, Ilkley, York). The quality of food is very high, and all made by Betty's own bakery in Harrogate. The uniformed waitresses give efficient and friendly service, and the café is very popular and busy. Several excellent tea blends are available.

Pot of tea £1.14, afternoon tea £2.90
Open all year, every day, 9am (10am on Sun) – 5.30pm
[1] [3]

NORTHWICH   Cheshire   Map 07 SJ67

Bratts Coffee Shop
2–6 Witton Street
Tel (0606) 43344

Situated on the second floor of this town-centre department store, Bratts offers various homemade biscuits, flapjacks and cakes, locally-made cream cakes, as well as speciality homemade scones. A choice of quality tea blends is available.

Pot of tea 42p
Open all year, Mon – Sat, 9.30am – 5.30pm (closed Wed afternoon)
Lunches available

NOTTINGHAM   Nottinghamshire   Map 08 SK54

Jessops and Sons
Victoria Centre
Tel (0602) 418282

This good department store has a comfortable restaurant on the second floor which is a well known and popular meeting place throughout the day. Afternoon and high teas are served by efficient waitresses. Homemade scones, toasted teacakes and cream cakes are on offer and there is a choice of blends of tea.

Pot of tea and scone £1.25
Open all year except bank holidays, Tue – Sat, 10am – 5pm (late night shopping Wed)

NOTTINGHAM   Nottinghamshire   Map 08 SK54

Raffles Tea Rooms
Angel Row
Tel (0602) 474344

These excellent Victorian-style tearooms are very nicely furnished, with carpeted floors, pictures of old Nottingham on the walls, and pretty lace cloths on the tables. Visitors are personally greeted at the door, and very pleasant and efficient staff are dressed in Victorian/Edwardian black and white uniforms. A bonus are the piano concerts at certain times of the day. A choice of excellent quality tea blends is available, served in Royal Worcester tea service. There is a most attractive display of delicious home-baked gâteaux and cakes.

Pot of tea £1, high tea £5.25
Open all year, Mon – Sat, 8am – 7pm, Sun 10am – 5pm
Breakfast and lunch available
[1] [3]

NOTTINGHAM   Nottinghamshire   Map 08 SK54

Savoy Hotel
Mansfield Road
Tel (0602) 602621

This four-star hotel is on the A60, only a mile from the city centre and has good parking facilities. Afternoon tea is served in a comfortable lounge, and consists of fresh sandwiches, scones and tea.

Set tea £1.95
Open every day, serving tea in the afternoons

OAKHAM   Leicestershire   Map 04 SK80

The Coffee Pot 13–15 Market Place Tel (0572) 723130	Pleasant ground-floor cottage-style premises, set at the rear of an art gallery with lots of country bric-à-brac on display. Homemade cakes, scones and teacakes are served, with some light meals and a choice of tea blends. Tea is properly presented with good china.	Pot of tea 50p Open all year, Mon – Sat, 10am – 4.30pm Light meals

---

OAKHAM   Leicestershire   Map 04 SK80

Muffins 9 Mill Street Tel (0572) 723501	A simple, bright cottage-style tearoom. Muffins serves light meals, teas and coffees. Homemade scones, muffins, teacakes and assorted cakes and gâteaux are available. Various tea blends are nicely presented with pretty crockery and a matching teapot.	Pot of tea 60p, cream tea £1.60 Open all year, Mon – Sat, 9am – 4.45pm (Sun Mar – Oct only 2.30pm – 5.30pm) Light meals

---

OAKHAM   Leicestershire   Map 04 SK80

Normanton Park Hotel Tel Stamford (0780) 720315	This former 18th-century coach house is all that is left of Normanton Hall. Situated in beautiful countryside on the south shore of Rutland Water, it has been transformed into a very pleasant hotel, including a popular coffee lounge with seating on the ground floor and two gallery levels. Homemade cakes and scones are served and a range of toasted sandwiches and ice creams.	Pot of tea 85p, set teas £1.60 – £3.80 Open all year, every day, 9am – 6.30pm 1 2 3 &

OAKHAM   Leicestershire   Map 04 SK80

Orchard Cuisine The Maltings Mill Street Tel (0572) 3435	These simple but pleasant ground floor premises adjoin a bread and cake shop, close to the town centre. Leaf tea is served from attractive crockery, and a choice of blends is available. Cakes, scones and teacakes, some homemade, are offered, as well as light snacks.	Pot of tea 45p, set teas from £1.95 Open all year, every day, 8.45am – 5pm Mon – Sat, 11am – 5pm Sun and bank holidays Light meals

---

OLDHAM   Greater Manchester   Map 07 SD90

King John Café Restaurant Kings Hall King Street Tel 061–633 7088	A spacious café restaurant above a shoe market in the centre of town, café-style tables and hanging plants. A good range of hot and cold dishes is served, and there is a colourful ice cream bar selling homemade ice cream. Cakes, scones, gâteaux, sausage rolls and meat pies are available, with a choice of tea blends.	Pot of tea 65p Open all year, Mon – Sat, 9am – 5.30pm Lunch

---

OSWESTRY   Shropshire   Map 07 SJ22

**Gerrards Cake Shop
and Coffee Lounge**
22 Bailey Street
Tel (0691) 662156

A small area on two levels at the rear of the cake shop counter, the coffee lounge has polished tables and wheel-back chairs. Homemade traditional country cakes are served: assorted pastries, scones, teacakes and bara brith.

Pot of tea and cake around
£1.30
Open all year, Mon – Sat,
9am – 5pm (4.30pm Sat)

OXFORD   Oxfordshire   Map 04 SP50

Randolph Hotel
Beaumont Street
Tel (0865) 247481

The Randolph is a large Gothic-style, city-centre hotel of the mid-Victorian period. Major renovation of the ground floor public rooms will be completed by the end of the summer season. Teas are served in public lounges, and also in the Coffee Shop and Buttery. Pastries, scones, sandwiches and muffins are available, with a choice of tea blends.

Cream tea £3.75, full high
tea £5.75
Open all year, every day,
3pm – 5.30pm
[1] [2] [3]

PEEBLES   Borders   *Peeblesshire*   Map 11 NT24

**Kailzie Gardens
Restaurant**
Kailzie
Tel (0721) 20007

Kailzie Gardens, Art Gallery and Waterfowl Pond, now open to the public, are situated within a private estate in a beautiful position on the River Tweed. The licensed restaurant, in the former stables, offers morning coffee, lunch and afternoon tea in congenial surroundings. The homemade scones, gâteaux and meringues should not be missed.

Set tea £2.25
Open Mar – Oct, every
day, 11 am – 5.30pm
Lunch
[&]

PEEBLES   Borders   *Peeblesshire*   Map 11 NT24

Sunflower
4 The Bridgegate
Tel (0721) 22420

This small licensed restaurant and craft shop just off the High Street has lots of bric-à-brac and paintings for sale. Excellent light meals, vegetarian dishes, morning coffee and afternoon tea are served in each of four small dining rooms. Homemade scones, bread, cakes and gâteaux are available, with a choice of speciality teas.

Pot of tea 40p – 55p
Open all year, Mon – Sat,
9.30am – 5.30pm
Light meals

PENARTH   South Glamorgan   Map 03 ST17

**Windsor Tea
Gardens**
Ludlow Lane

This is a pretty establishment with a pink theme – carpet, wall panels, drapes and table linen, with modern cane furniture. Snacks and some light meals such as salads and jacket potatoes are served. For afternoon tea there are Welsh cakes, walnut slices, pastries, scones and teacakes.

Pot of tea 40p
Open all year, Mon – Sat,
9.30am – 5pm
Light meals

PENMAENMAWR   Gwynedd   Map 06 SH77

**Y Bedol Bach Tea
Room**
Capelulo
Tel (0492) 623670

At the foot of the Sychnant Pass, this attractive
black-and-white building houses the village shop and
post office, and also offers a range of hot snacks and
homemade cakes and scones, and, of course, bara
brith. Cosy and bright, with fresh flowers and pot
plants, the welcome here is warm and genuine.

Pot of tea 40p, cream tea
£1.70
Open all year, every day,
8.30am – 7pm (half-day
closing Wed in winter)

PETERBOROUGH   Cambridgeshire   Map 04 TL19

Maxines
Queens Gate Shopping
Centre
Tel (0733) 48620

At this popular, Continental-style café in a busy shopping
centre, polite, uniformed staff serve the tables inside
and out in the shopping mall. Morning coffee, snacks,
light lunches and afternoon tea are served. A good
selection of scones, pastries, cakes and pancakes is
available.

Pot of tea 65p, cream tea
£1.75
Open all year, Mon – Sat,
9am – 5pm (teas not
served 11.30am – 2pm)

PITLOCHRY   Tayside   *Perthshire*   Map 14 NN95

The Old Smithy
154 Atholl Road
Tel (0796) 2356

This family-run business includes a tearoom and
restaurant combined with a shop selling quality
fashions, crafts and gifts. The cottage-style tearoom is
pleasantly decorated and the walls are hung with
prints, many of which are for sale. Open sandwiches
are a speciality, with homebaked scones, carrot cake
and apple pie. A choice of tea blends is offered.

Pot of tea 45p
Open Feb – Dec, winter
Mon – Fri 10 am – 5 pm,
summer Mon – Sun 10am
– 8pm

POOLE   Dorset   Map 04 SZ09

Hospitality Inn
The Quay
Tel (0202) 666800

This modern commercial hotel on the quayside has
good views over Poole Harbour. Refreshments are
served in the first floor lounge. There is a tray service
for tea, with a choice of Earl Grey or China tea, as well
as the standard blend. Homemade cakes, scones and
sandwiches are served.

Afternoon tea £2.50
Open all year, every day,
3pm – 5pm for tea

POOLE   Dorset   Map 04 SZ09

Salterns
38 Salterns Way
Lilliput
Tel (0202) 707321

This modernised hotel overlooks the marina with
comfortable, tastefully appointed public rooms.
There is also a patio with fine views of the harbour.
Homemade cakes and scones are served, with a
choice of tea blends.

Afternoon tea £3.50
Open all year, every day,
3pm – 5pm for tea
1 2 3

POOLE　Dorset　Map 04 SZ09

Towngate Café
Dolphin Hotel
High Street
Tel (0202) 673612

Part of the Dolphin Hotel and situated in the main shopping precinct, this is a modern conservatory-style coffee shop with hanging baskets and cane furniture. Light meals, sandwiches, scones, cakes and pastries are available on a self-service basis.

Afternoon tea £1.60
Open all year, every day,
9am – 5.30pm
Light meals
1 2 3

POOLEY BRIDGE　Cumbria　Map 12 NY42

Heughscar
Tel (08536) 453

This corner bed-and-breakfast establishment has the dining room properly set up for tea, and offers fresh sandwiches, various types of scone, biscuits and cakes. There is a good choice of speciality teas.

Pot of tea, 45p, afternoon
tea £2.20
Open all year, every day
Apr – Oct, Sun only Nov –
Mar, 10am – 5.30pm

POOLEY BRIDGE　Cumbria　Map 12 NY42

Sharrow Bay Hotel
Tel (08536) 301 478

This unique hotel enjoys a superb position on the shores of Lake Ullswater, with wonderful views over the lake and surrounding fells. For the past forty years and more the hotel's owners, Francis Coulson and Brian Sack have provided their unique blend of hospitality and excellent cooking to an ever-growing and appreciative clientèle. Afternoon tea is served either in the lounge or in the conservatory, and only a small number of non-resident guests can be accommodated. Pastries, scones and cakes are so light that they melt in the mouth, and the service and the china are both equally fine.

Full afternoon tea from
£6.50
Open Mar – Nov, every
day, 4 – 5pm

PORTESHAM　Dorset　Map 03 SY68

Millmead Country Hotel
Tel (0305) 871432

A modern building attached to the owners' house in this quiet little village. The dining room for non-residents is a light, airy conservatory with garden-style furniture and many attractive plants. Cakes and scones are served with a choice of tea blends. Smoking is not permitted.

Afternoon tea about £1.65
Open all year, every day,
2.30pm – 6.30pm for tea

PORT TALBOT West Glamorgan Map 03 SS79

Gossip
1 Riverside Shops
Aberavon Shopping
Centre
Tel (0639) 890622

This small café is on two floors in a busy town shopping centre. Light meals are available with some homemade gâteaux, cheesecake and teacakes.

Tea and cake around 95p
Open all year, Mon – Sat,
9am – 5pm
Lunch

PRESTATYN Clwyd Map 06 SJ08

Bryn Gwalia Inn
Gronant Road
Tel (074 56) 2442

This busy inn is open all day and extemely popular at lunchtime with local customers. The interior is pretty and homely, with sofas and easy chairs, and a large array of bric-à-brac. Cream teas are served and homemade biscuits and sponge cake are also available.

Pot of tea 45p, cream tea
£1.85
Open 2.30pm – 6pm for
afternoon tea
Lunch, dinner
⌖

PRESTEIGNE Powys Map 03 SO36

**Radnorshire Arms
Hotel**
High Street
Tel (0544) 267406

Attractively positioned amid lawns and gardens, this half-timbered inn has public rooms of great character. Lounge service is available for afternoon tea.

Cream tea £2.50
Open all year, every day
1 2 3

RANGEMORE Staffordshire Map 07 SK12

Byrkley Park Centre
(5 miles west of
Burton-on-Trent, off
A38 beyond Tatenhill)
Tel (0283) 716467

Converted stables house this very attractive café set in the middle of a popular garden and craft centre. Winner of a healthy eating award in 1989, the homebaking is excellent, with many types of sponge cake, fruit slices and traditional specialities like Bakewell tart featured on the menu.

Cream tea £1.60
Open every day, Apr –
Aug, 9am – 6pm (9pm,
Thu, Fri, Sat), Sep – Mar,
9am – 5pm
1 3 ⌖

RHOS-ON-SEA Clwyd Map 06 SC88

Penrhos Restaurant
53 Llandudno Road
Tel Colwyn Bay (0492)
49547

A small restaurant with pretty lace cloths, exposed beams bedecked with a jug collection and a loud chiming clock. There is also a small patio outside. Popular with both locals and tourists, light snacks and meals are served throughout the day. Pies, pastries and scones are homemade while cakes and gâteaux are from a local bakery.

Pot of tea 35p
Open all year, Mon – Fri
9am – 5.30pm, Sat 9am –
2pm, Sun lunch only

RHOS-ON-SEA   Clwyd   Map 06 SC88

Summers Restaurant & Tearoom Rhos Road Tel Colwyn Bay (0492) 44790	A bright, cheerful restaurant close to the promenade, with pretty floral wallpaper, beamed ceiling and lace tablecloths. Light savoury snacks, scones and cakes are served with a selection of gâteaux and pastries from the trolley. A choice of tea blends is available.	Pot of tea 45p, cake 80p – £1.10 Open all year, Tue – Sun (Mon – Sun high season), 10am – 5pm winter, 10am – 8pm summer

---

RICHMOND   North Yorkshire   Map 07 N210

Mary's 5–6 Trinity Church Square Tel (0748) 4052	Mary's is situated in the main square over a very good delicatessen which supplies the tea and coffee blends and cooked meats. Hot dishes are served as well as homemade cakes, scones, sandwiches and teacakes. Seven blends of leaf tea are available.	Full tea £2.50 Open all year, every day, 9am – 5.45pm

---

RINGWOOD   Hampshire   Map 04 SU10

Daisy Darling 35 High Street Tel (0425) 474563	A single-fronted restaurant in the centre of Ringwood with a cottagey atmosphere, padded Windsor chairs and Indian tree pattern china. A comprehensive menu of hot meals, snacks and speciality ice creams is offered. Commercially produced cakes, scones and pastries are available for afternoon tea.	Pot of tea 45p, cream tea £1.75 Open all year, Mon – Sat, 9am – 5pm (9am – 11pm Fri – Sat) Lunch, dinner 1 3 ♿

ROMSEY   Hampshire   Map 04 SU32

Cobweb Tearooms 49 The Hundred Tel (0794) 516434	Attractive, beamed tearooms with green-clothed tables and captain's chairs. The table is laden with homemade cakes and cream teas, and a sweet trolley displays dishes such as hazlenut torte, pavlova and cheesecake. Lunches are also served.	Cream tea £1.50 Open all year, (except 2 weeks Sep and 1 week Christmas), Tue – Sat, 10am – 5.30pm Lunches

---

ROSS-ON-WYE   Hereford and Worcester   Map 03 SO62

Copperfields 29 Gloucester Road Tel (0989) 67734	Pleasant, bright ground floor teashop, part of a delicatessen and pâtisserie, popular with shoppers and tourists alike. Scones, teacakes, cream cakes and gâteaux, many of which are baked on the premises, are served. There is also a good range of hot and cold snacks and a choice of tea blends is offered. Smoking is not permitted.	Tea 59p Open Jan – Dec, Mon – Sat, 9am – 5pm Hot and cold snacks

ROSS-ON-WYE   Hereford and Worcester   Map 03 SO26

| **Pengethley Manor** Tel (0989) 87211 | A lovely Georgian manor house, now a country-house hotel, situated in 15 acres of grounds and gardens with splendid views of the surrounding countryside, four miles north-west of the town on the A49. Home baking, sandwiches and strawberry teas in season are served with a choice of tea blends, presented in silver teapots with Wedgwood china. | Pot of tea £1, set teas from £3.75 Open all year, every day, 3pm – 6pm 〔1〕 〔2〕 〔3〕 |

RUTHIN   Clwyd   Map 06 SJ15

| **Bay Tree** Ruthin Craft Centre Tel (08242) 2121 | A modern self-service café in the middle of the large Craft Centre, the Bay Tree has a modern décor, with a quarry-tiled floor, pine furniture and a small outside patio area. Teas, light snacks and quite substantial lunches are served. Sandwiches, scones and bara brith are available with a selection of gâteaux and Danish pastries. | Pot of tea 40p, afternoon tea £1.70 Open all year, every day, 10.30am – 5pm (noon – 5pm Sun) Lunches |

RUTHIN   Clwyd   Map 06 SJ15

| **Ruthin Castle Tearoom** Ruthin Castle Tel (08242) 2664 | A simply but prettily furnished tearoom, part of the Ruthin Castle Hotel, formerly a large impressive sandstone castle, parts of which date back to 1296. The busy tearoom serves homemade fruit cake, sponges and scones, with a choice of tea blends, and the matching leaf-pattern crockery is particularly attractive. | Pot of tea 75p, afternoon tea £2.70 Open all year, every day, 2.30 – 5.30pm |

RYE   East Sussex   Map 05 TQ92

| **Mermaid Inn** Mermaid Street Tel (0797) 223065 | Afternoon tea is served in the Tudor Room of this welcoming medieval inn which dates from 1157, and has wonderful beamed and oak-panelled public rooms. Soup and sandwiches are available for light meals, and for tea homebaked scones are served with a choice of good professionally made pâtisserie. | Pot of tea and biscuits £1, cream tea £3 Open Easter – Sep, every day, noon – 5pm Lunches 〔1〕 〔2〕 〔3〕 |

ST AGNES   Cornwall and Isles of Scilly   Map 02 SW75

| **Sunholme Hotel** Tel (087255) 2318 | A teapot sign at the end of the drive points the way to a well-presented and friendly small hotel on St Agnes Beacon. Here you can enjoy superb views of countryside and coast as you sample home-made scones and a freshly made pot of Earl Grey or Indian tea. | Cream tea £1.70 Open Apr – Oct, every day,3 – 5pm Bar snacks |

ST ALBANS   Herts   Map 04 TL10

Dahlia Coffee Shop
Aylett Nurseries Ltd
The North Orbital
Road (A405)
London Colney
Tel (0727) 22255

This attractive, conservatory-style tea/coffee shop,
with its pleasantly airy atmosphere and abundance of
plants, offers Earl Grey and camomile teas as
alternatives to the more traditional blends, whilst
friendly, attentive staff serve a good range of
homemade scones and cakes as well as quiches, ròlls
and sandwiches.

Tea 45p – 55p per person
Open all year, every day,
except Christmas Day and
Boxing Day, 9.30am – 5pm

ST ALBANS   Herts   Map 04 TL10

Noke Thistle Hotel
Watford Road
Tel (0727) 54252

An attractive hotel, retaining much of its Victorian
charm and cosy atmosphere, offering refreshments in
both comfortable lounge and bar. Tea is properly
made and well presented, with a choice of China, Earl
Grey, Assam or Darjeeling blends. A range of
croissants, sandwiches, pastries, gâteaux and home-
baked cookies is available – or you can indulge in a
cream tea.

Pot of tea £1.50 per
person
Cream tea £3.50
Open every day (all day)

ST ALBANS   Herts   Map 04 TL10

Wafffles
39 St Giles Street
Kingsbury Watermill
St Michael's Street
Tel (0727) 53502

A characterful tearoom with open fires and exposed
beams is set in an Elizabethan house adjoining a
working watermill which has been converted into a
museum; guests can also browse in the art gallery and
gift shop. Predictably, the establishment specialises in
a wide variety of waffles – both sweet and savoury –
and it offers a good choice of speciality teas.

Tea 55p per person
Open all year, Wed – Sun,
11.00am (12.00 Sundays
and bank holidays) –
5.00pm (6.00pm Summer)

ST ANDREWS   Fife *Fife*   Map 12 NO51

**The Merchant's
House**
49 South Street
Tel (0334) 72595

Dating back to the 17th century, this fine town house
has been beautifully restored and retains old painted
ceilings and the original vaults, now glass-roofed to
give a bright, airy atmosphere. The range of home-
baking is excellent and there is a wide choice of
China, Indian and herbal teas. Service is good and the
surroundings full of interest.

Pot of tea 50p, scones,
shortbread etc. from 30p
Open every day, Apr –
Oct, Mon – Wed 10am –
9pm, Thu – Sat 10am –
10pm, Sun 10am – 7pm,
Nov – Mar, every day 10am
– 5.30pm
Other meals also served

ST ANDREWS   Fife *Fife*   Map 12 NO51

Mill Ring Restaurant
Clayton Caravan Park
(between Dairsie and
Guardbridge, 5 miles
west of St Andrews)
Tel (0334) 870630

The restaurant is as popular with passing customers
as with caravanners in the park, and has the added
attraction of a children's play area outside. 'Worth a
visit for Patsy's scones alone', says our Inspector, but
there is a wide range of other good home-baking, all
very good value.

Pot of tea 40p, cakes 20 –
68p
Open Mar – Oct, every
day, 8.30am – 7pm
Light refreshments also
served

ST ANDREWS   Fife *Fife*   Map 12 NO51

Old Course Hotel
Old Station Road
Tel (0334) 74371

Afternoon tea is served in the Observation Lounge, so-called for its splendid view across the Royal and Ancient Golf Course to the sea beyond. Staff are courteous, attentive and professional, and there is a wide choice both of good baking and blends of tea, properly made and correctly served.

Afternoon tea £6.50, tea and cake from about £2.75
Open all year, every day, 7am – 6.30pm
Light refreshments also served

ST CLEARS   Dyfed   Map 02 SN21

County Tea Rooms
Pentre Road
Tel (0994) 231061

In a small room furnished with polished tables and cottage-style chairs you can enjoy a good, traditional cup of tea accompanied by a scone, custard slice or Danish pastry – or perhaps by sandwiches or a hot snack if you require something more substantial. Staff are particularly friendly here.

Cup of tea and Danish Pastry 95p
Open all year, Mon – Sat

ST CLEARS   Dyfed   Map 02 SN21

Forge Hotel and Restaurant
Tel (0994) 230300

This pleasant, small, and personally-run motel is set conveniently back from the A40 and is a most welcome stopping place. Meals, including cream teas are served in the comfortable bar, and they make a very good cup of tea.

Cream tea £1.40
Open every day, teas served in the afternoons
Other meals also served

ST GERRANS   Cornwall and Isles of Scilly   Map 02 SW93

Turnpike Cottage Antiques and Tearooms
The Square
Tel (087258) 853

Beyond the stable door of this pretty white cottage is a delightful small tearoom – just the place for a delicious Cornish cream tea after an afternoon on the nearby beaches around Portscatho. Cakes are served in the traditional way on porcelain cake stands, while the other pieces of porcelain and small antiques which decorate the room are all for sale.

Cream tea £1.70
Open all year, Tue – Sun 3 – 6pm
Lunches Easter – October 11am – 1.30pm

ST IVES   Cornwall and Isles of Scilly   Map 02 SW54

Bumbles Tea Shop
Digby Square
Tel (0736) 797977

The Georgian frontage of this pretty, cottage-style tearoom is complemented by the quality of its interior, and there are pleasant views from all windows. Guests not tempted by the cream tea can choose from a range of sandwiches, scones and cakes.

Tea 45p per cup
Open all year, Thur – Tue, 10.00am – 5.00pm

ST IVES   Cornwall and Isles of Scilly   Map 02 SW54

Coasters Tea Shop
15 St Andrews Street
Tel (0736) 794184

This compact, granite-walled shop near the harbour wall, its exposed beams complemented by polished tables, benches and wheelback chairs, offers a selection of fresh scones, date and walnut bread, peanut, rich chocolate and yogurt cakes accompanied by a range of teas which includes Darjeeling, Earl Grey and some herbal blends, all served with a choice of milk or lemon.

Pot of tea 50p cream tea £1.90
Open Easter – end Oct, every day, 10am – 6pm
Light snacks

ST IVES   Cornwall and Isles of Scilly   Map 02 SW54

Cobblestones Coffee House
5 St Andrews Street
Tel (0736) 797613

A cottage-style teashop with exposed beams, polished wood tables and wheelback chairs, commanding views along the coast from its picture window. Cobblestones serves an enjoyable cream tea with homemade scones and a good pot of tea.

Pot of tea 40p cream tea £1.40
Open all year, every day, 9am – 5pm
Snacks from 95p – £2.10

SALCOMBE   Devon   Map 03 SX73

Bolt Head Hotel
Tel (054884) 3751

In the comfortable lounges of this friendly hotel, with its fine views across the estuary, you can enjoy a typical Devon cream tea in which appetising sandwiches are succeeded by homemade scones and pastries, courteous staff offering a choice of traditional, Darjeeling or Earl Grey tea.

Cream tea £2.95
Open mid May – end Oct, every day, 11am – 6pm

SALCOMBE   Devon   Map 03 SX73

Marine Hotel
Tel (054884) 3554

A large, traditionally-styled hotel with unrestricted views across the estuary offers quality afternoon teas in its spaciously comfortable public rooms. Guests can opt for the cream tea or take their pick from a wide selection of homemade scones, pastries and cakes accompanied by a well-flavoured, correctly-brewed pot of tea, whether it be Lapsang, Darjeeling, Earl Grey or a more traditional blend.

Set tea £3.50
Open all year, every day, 2.30 – 5.30pm

SALISBURY   Wiltshire   Map 04 SU12

Michael Snell Tea Rooms
8 Saint Thomas's Square
Tel (0722) 336037

Homemade gâteaux, cream cakes and pastries are the speciality of tearooms which take in the old town-miller's house to the front and a former church school at the rear. Earl Grey, Darjeeling, Lapsang and Assam teas are available, all carefully brewed and attractively served by helpful staff.

Tea from 53p cream tea £2.05
Open all year, Mon – Sat, 9am – 5.30pm

SALISBURY   Wiltshire   Map 04 SU12

Reeve the Baker Butcher Row Tel (0722) 20367	This two-storey corner shop overlooking the market place is supplied by its own bakery and offers a selection of set teas served by friendly young staff; Earl Grey and Old England teas offer alternatives to the more traditional Indian blend.	Set teas £1.75 – £2.50 Open all year, Mon – Sat, 9am – 5.30pm

---

SALISBURY   Wiltshire   Map 04 SU12

White Hart St John Street Tel (0722) 27476	In the pleasant, open-plan lounge of this city-centre hotel you can enjoy a set tea which complements homemade scones and cakes with a good cup of Earl Grey, Grosvenor or Indian tea, properly brewed and served in a china pot.	Set teas from £1.95 – £2.75 and £3.75 Open all year, every day, 3pm – 5.30pm

---

SEAHOUSES   Northumberland   Map 12 NU23

Koffee and Kreme 15 Main Street Tel (0665) 720278	The owner of this neat, homely, little tearoom personally supervises the ministrations of its friendly staff and also the production of such homemade delicacies as scones, shortbread, lemon meringue pie, sponges and gâteaux; hot snacks are also available. Tea is properly made and accompanied by hot water for 'topping up', though no choice of blends is offered.	Open all year, every day, 9am – 4.30pm (winter) or up to 9pm (summer) Hot dishes served all day

---

SEAHOUSES   Northumberland   Map 12 NU23

Seafarers Main Street Tel (0665) 720931	Neat, spacious and conveniently situated in the centre of the town, this family-run tearoom accompanies a good, traditional pot of tea with a range of scones, cakes, teabreads and preserves that are all homemade on the premises. Spotless surroundings, attractive tablecloths and friendly service combine to create a homely atmosphere.	Tea 35p Open Easter – Oct, every day, 10am – 6pm (Sundays 1am – 6pm) Coffee and light lunches

---

SEATON   Devon   Map 03 SY29

The Kettle 15 Fore Street Tel (0297) 20428	A 400-year-old, town-centre, terraced house retains much of its original character, complementing the old oak beams with comfortable pine furniture. Darjeeling, Ceylon, Earl Grey and Indian teas – correctly brewed in china pots – are available, and guests are offered a choice of Plain Tea, Cottage Tea or Cream Tea, with home-baked scones and cakes.	Set teas £1.15 – £1.75 Open Apr – Oct, Fri – Wed, 10am – 4pm and (in summer) 6.30pm – 9pm Coffee

---

SELWORTHY GREEN Somerset   Map 03 SS94

Periwinkle Cottage
(near Porlock)
Tel (0643) 862 769

This pretty little thatched cottage is everyone's dream of a traditional teashop, with roses and periwinkles in the garden, looking out on the village green and across to Exmoor. Winner of the National Tea Council Award in 1988, it naturally serves a good pot of tea, and several blends are available, including some fruit-flavoured and herb teas. Scones and cakes are freshly baked on the premises, and the scones, served with the local clotted cream, are even more irresistible than the delicious cakes. This is fine walking country so you can either enjoy a walk to work up an appetite for your tea, or to disperse the calories afterwards. No smoking in the café.

Pot of tea 50p, cream tea £1.75, cakes from 75p
Open mid Mar – Oct, Tue – Sun (and also bank holiday Mons) 10am – 5pm
Morning coffee and lunch also served

SHIPDHAM Norfolk   Map 05 TL90

Shipdham Place
Church Close
Tel (0362) 820303

This country-house hotel, dating from the 17th century, was formerly the village rectory. Afternoon tea is served in either the drawing room or the parlour – both tastefully decorated rooms with comfortable chesterfields, chairs and sofas, giving a tranquil setting in which to enjoy the tempting homemade biscuits, cakes and scones.

Set tea £2.50
Open all year, every day, 3 – 5pm
1 3

SHREWSBURY Shropshire   Map 07 SJ41

Casa Fina
St Austins Street
Tel (0743) 232388

The proprietor of a rather chic establishment specialising in imported furniture, ceramics and objets d'art has utilised the floor above to create a teashop which is conveniently close to town centre and bus station. Here, guests enjoy a good cup of tea, either Indian, Earl Grey, Darjeeling or China, accompanied by sandwiches and a selection of homemade scones, cakes and gâteaux.

Tea 65p, set tea £2.40
Open all year, Mon – Sat, 9am – 5pm
Light cooked meals

SHREWSBURY   Shropshire   Map 07 SJ41

Intermission Restaurant and Café
Pride Hill Shopping Centre
Tel (0743) 25393

This very pleasant, smart establishment – part of larger premises which include a self-service restaurant, but operated separately – stands in a new, modern shopping centre at the heart of the city. Savouries, scones and a wide variety of cakes and pastries are available, with a choice of Indian, Darjeeling, Assam and Earl Grey tea.

Tea 57p
Cream tea £1.55
Open all year, Mon – Sat, 8.30am – 5.30pm
Grills, brunch, omelettes, pasta, salads

SHREWSBURY   Shropshire   Map 07 SJ41

Music Hall
The Square
Tel (0743) 58057

Pleasant, ground-floor premises in a town-centre theatre house a tearoom where friendly waitresses serve a well-made, traditional cup of tea with a range of sandwiches, scones, cakes and pastries; a good selection of light, cooked meals is also available. Coach parties and functions can be catered for by arrangement.

Tea 40p
Open all year, every day (except Sun, Nov – Easter), 10am – 5pm (3.30pm Sun)

SHREWSBURY   Shropshire   Map 07 SJ41

Poppy's Café and Teashop
19 Princess Street
Tel (0743) 232307

A simple but charming little town-centre teashop is housed in premises where fire-engine horses were stabled in the 18th century, and a pleasant courtyard area and stable annexe are brought into use in summer. Freshly brewed Earl Grey, Darjeeling, Assam and caffeine-free teas are available as well as the more traditional Indian blend, with scones, teacakes, flapjacks and pastries.

Tea 50p
Set tea £2.30
Open all year, Mon – Sat, 9.45am – 4.30pm (7pm in summer)

SHREWSBURY   Shropshire   Map 07 SJ41

Tiffin Coffee House
30 The Parade
St Mary's Place
Tel (0743) 247350

In part of what was once a hospital but is now a pleasant indoor shopping centre, with an attractive terrace overlooking the River Severn, friendly waitresses serve sandwiches (including the toasted variety), salads and snacks; tea, whether Indian, Earl Grey or China, is properly brewed in crockery pots.

Tea from 40p
Open all year, Mon – Sat, 9.30am – 5pm
Coffee, snacks

SHREWSBURY   Shropshire   Map 07 SJ41

Traitors Gate Bistro
St Mary's
Water Lane (off Castle Street)
Tel (0743) 249152

These fascinating basement premises dating back to the 12th century and retaining their original arched-brick, cellar ceilings are actually part of the castle walls – the café name commemorating the admittance of the Parliamentarians through a river gate during the Civil War. Properly made and attractively served tea is accompanied by homemade cakes, and a full range of bistro-type meals is also available.

Tea 50p
Open all year, Mon – Sat, 10am – 11.30am and 2.30 – 4pm

SIDBURY   Devon   Map 03 SY19

The Old Bakery
(Three miles from
Sidmouth)
Tel (03957) 319

This attractive tearoom, housed in a 400-year-old building, stands in the village centre and is well placed for visitors to Sidmouth and other coastal resorts, as well as to the nearby Donkey Sanctuary. There are comfortable sitting rooms as well as the formal tearoom, and a garden for the fine weather. Cakes, scones and shortbreads are all delicious, but the speciality is meringues with clotted cream – impossible to resist, so forget your diet. There are three different set teas as well as the daily selection of cakes and to drink, a choice of the house tea, Earl Grey, or China with lemon.

Open Apr – Sep, every day except Wed and Sun, 10am – 12.30pm, 2 – 6pm No smoking in the tearoom

SIDMOUTH   Devon   Map 03 SY18

The Chattery
67 High Street
Tel (0395) 515853

The double-fronted shop stands in the town centre, close to the Post Office, its interior made homely by hanging plants, pictures and ornaments. Both the Plain Tea and the Devon Cream Tea include a good selection of homemade scones and cakes, served with a choice of Indian or Earl Grey tea.

Plain Tea £1.50 Devon Cream Tea £1.75 Open all year, Mon – Sat (Sun in summer), 10am (11am on Sun) – 5pm Lunchtime dishes

SIDMOUTH   Devon   Map 03 SY18

Victoria Hotel
The Esplanade
Tel (0395) 512651

In the spacious, comfortable lounge areas of this fine Victorian hotel – which overlooks the sea from a convenient location only a short, level walk from the town centre – you can choose from a range of set afternoon teas with homebaked cakes and a selection of blends which includes China, Darjeeling and Earl Grey.

Pot of tea £1 per person, set teas from £1.75 Open every day, 24 hours Lunches and dinners

SIMONSBATH   Somerset   Map 03 SS73

Simonsbath House Hotel
Tel (064383) 259

A 300-year-old hotel at the heart of the Forest of Exmoor offers a welcome break for walkers and tourists, serving teas in a large, comfortable lounge with deep settees and open fires in winter, or in the garden on warmer days. Indian, Earl Grey and Darjeeling teas accompany a wide choice of scones and cakes – with clotted cream as an additional temptation!

Pot of tea 60p, cream teas from £1.95 Open end Jan – 1 Dec, every day, 3 – 5.30pm Morning coffee and light lunches

SITTINGBOURNE   Kent   Map 05 TQ97

Ferns Court Café Norton Ash Garden Centre Norton Cross Roads Tel (0795) 521034	This attractive café bar – part of a large garden-centre on the A2, but screened off so that you can eat inside or out – serves an excellent lunchtime selection which includes a Ploughman's and an appetising, authentic Pork Pie Salad. In the afternoons, breakfast, Earl Grey, Darjeeling and herbal teas are available to accompany a range of homemade cakes and scones.	Cream tea £1.20 Open all year, every day,

SIX ASHES   Shropshire   Map 07 SO78

Six Ashes Tea Room (between Bridgnorth and Stourbridge on A458) Tel (038488) 216	This neat, small tearoom is behind a craft shop which sells a wide range of giftware and is a handy stopover on a journey. Scones, cakes, gâteaux and pies are homemade and very acceptable. Cream teas are popular.	Cream tea £1.80 Open all year, Tue – Sat, 10am – 5pm

SKYE, ISLE OF   Highland *Inverness-shire*   Map 13 NG52

Pipers Moon Luib Tel (04712) 594	This neat and simple little tearoom is run by a very charming and friendly owner who makes extremely good scones and delicious fresh salmon sandwiches. There is a range of craft and knitware for sale.	Open 3rd week Mar – 3rd week Oct, every day, 9am – 6pm

SKYE OF CURR   Highland   *Inverness-shire*, Map 14 NH02

Cloot Dumpling **Tearoom** Speyside Heather Centre and Scottish Heather Heritage Centre Dulnain Bridge Tel (047985) 359	The tearoom takes its name from a traditional Scots delicacy that it actually serves – a fruit dumpling, usually eaten as a pudding, but also suitable for teatime when sliced cold. This homely establishment, with its pine furniture, chequered tablecloths and wood-burning stove, also serves home-baked cakes and various scones and jams, with a choice of Earl Grey, Assam, Darjeeling or herbal tea by the cup, mug or pot.	Tea from 40p Open Nov – Feb, Thu – Sat, 9am – 5pm, Mar – Oct, every day, 9am – 6pm

SOUTH MOLTON   Devon   Map 03 SS72

The Corn Dolly
115A East Street
Tel (07695) 2645

The tearoom adjoins a craft shop in the centre of the town. It is a traditional, old, terraced building, with exposed beams and stonework and rush matting on the floor. The set teas are delicious, and include both savoury and sweet dishes. For the former, try Kings Ransom, a large toasted teacake with grilled Stilton cheese, or a Seafarers Tea, a hot fillet of smoked mackerel served with buttered toast and gooseberry sauce. There are also two special children's teas, with favourites like toast and marmite, jelly and ice-cream. The selection of teas includes Darjeeling, Earl Grey, Lapsang Souchong, Assam, or the house blend of Ceylon.

Cream tea £2.50
Open all year, Tue – Fri 9.30am – 5.30pm; Sat 10am – 5.30pm

SOUTH MOLTON   Devon   Map 03 SS72

The Parlour Tea Room
East Street
Tel (07695) 4144

Housed in an attractive Georgian building on the outskirts of the town, the tearooms are charmingly decorated with Laura Ashley fabrics and antique furniture. The owners, Mr and Mrs Koch, make their visitors extremely welcome, serving homemade scones, sponges, fruit cakes and pastries, with a good choice of blends of tea, properly made and served. This is an excellent place to stop for tea, and the town is a convenient centre for exploring the many attractions of North Devon. There is limited parking in the street outside the tearooms.

Pot of tea 80p
Open all year, Mon – Sat 8.30am – 6pm

SOUTHWELL   Nottinghamshire   Map 08 SK75

Gossips
King Street
Tel (0636) 815214

This two-storey tearoom in the main street – a bustling, popular meeting place – is also a baker's shop selling locally made cakes. Old oak beams are complemented by plain walls displaying pictures for sale, and by old church pew seating on the ground floor. Waitresses in black and white with coloured berets serve good, flavoursome Indian and Earl Grey tea.

Tea 50p – 55p, cream tea £1.95
Open all year, Mon – Sat (Sun in summer), 9am – 5pm
Coffee, salads and hot dishes

SOUTHWOLD   Suffolk   Map 05 TM57

Swan Hotel Market Place Tel (0502) 722186	Southwold must rank as the most attractive seaside town in Suffolk, and the Swan Hotel stands right at the centre. Afternoon teas are served in the comfortable lounge and although the winter menu is limited to scones and shortbread, there is more choice in summer. Darjeeling, Ceylon, Lapsang, Earl Grey and breakfast Tea are available.	Cream tea £3.50 Open all year, every day, 3 – 5.30pm 1 2 3 ♿

SPILSBY   Lincolnshire   Map O9 TF56

Buttercross Restaurant 18 Lower Market Tel (0790) 5347	A pleasant restaurant, housed in a Grade-two, listed Georgian building overlooking the market place, it serves lunches only from 1pm–2pm, but lighter snacks at other times. Friendly staff will serve you with either the set afternoon tea or a selection of scones and cakes and tea is freshly made and well presented, with Passion Fruit as well as more traditional blends.	Tea 40p – 50p, full afternoon tea £2.20 Open all year except Christmas, Mon, Wed – Sat, 10am – early afternoon and from 7.30pm Morning coffee, lunches

---

STAMFORD   Lincolnshire   Map 04 TF00

George Hotel St Martins Tel (0780) 55171	In a beautiful 16th-century inn retaining much of its historic charm and atmosphere, you can enjoy a good cup of freshly brewed tea – Indian, Assam, Darjeeling, Earl Grey or Camomile – in any of the pleasant public rooms or in a courtyard with hanging baskets and flower tubs. Friendly and courteous staff serve a good range of sandwiches, scones, tarts and cream cakes.	Cream tea £1.50 Open all year, every day, 9am – 10pm

---

STOCKPORT   Greater Manchester   Map 07 SJ88

Tiviots Restaurant and Tea Room Vernon Street Tel 061–477 20434	Set in a conservation area close to the town's historic market, yet adjoining the main shopping area, the tearoom boasts an exceptionally comprehensive list of teas, including examples from China, India, Ceylon and Africa as well as herbal infusions and such exotic fruit blends as Bitter Almond, all well-made and correctly served. Homemade delicacies include scones and fruit, carrot or orange cake.	Pot of tea 35 – 40p Open all year, Mon 9am – 5pm, Tue – Sat 9am – late pm, Sun 11am – 4pm Speciality coffee, snacks, special 4-course dinners

---

STONE   Staffordshire   Map 07 SJ93

Astaires 7A Radford Street Tel (0785) 815252	Whilst only a modest range of scones, teacakes and gâteaux – some items homebaked and some bought in – is offered here, the restaurant's clean, bright décor and the friendly helpfulness of the waitresses make it a pleasant place in which to enjoy a cup of their speciality tea. Snacks are served throughout the day, with an à la carte menu available in the evening.	Pot of tea 50p (80p for 2), speciality tea 30p per cup Open all year, Tue – Sat 9.30am – 3pm (may soon be later) Connoisseur Coffee, Sunday lunch, snacks, à la carte evening meals

STON EASTON   Avon   Map 03 ST65

Ston Easton Park
Nr. Bath
Tel Chewton Mendip
(O76121) 631

The hotel is a gracious Palladian mansion of real architectural distinction set in beautiful landscaped grounds not far from Bath. The Saloon has been described as 'the finest room in Somerset' and the tea laid out on side tables here echoes this description. Scones, clotted cream, strawberry jam, chocolate éclairs, strawberry tarts and Eccles cakes are amongst the wide selection to which you help yourself, and you are invited to take as much as you can eat for a set price. Tea (there is a choice of ten herbal infusions, as well as Earl Grey, Assam and Darjeeling) is served in silver pots from butlers' trays, and the cups are of fine china. Given suitable advance notice, the hotel will make up sumptuous picnic hampers with wine for you to take into the gardens.

Afternoon tea £5.50
Open all year, every day,
3.30 – 6pm

STONEHENGE   Wiltshire   Map 04 SU14

Underground Tea Rooms
Amesbury
Tel (0980) 22136

Not truly underground, but using the contours of the land to avoid obtruding on the skyline of Stonehenge, a purpose-built, single-storey café serves such typically British fare as rock cakes and bread pudding; counter service only is offered, but staff are polite and attentive, whilst tea is well-flavoured though served in paper cups.

Tea 30p
Open all year, every day,
9.30am – 6.30pm (4pm in winter)

STOURPORT-ON-SEVERN   Hereford and Worcester   Map 07 SO87

Tudor Tea Room
Bridge Street
Tel (02993) 2446

The café is at the back of the cake shop, and serves a selection of scones, cakes and fresh cream gâteaux. It is conveniently close to the riverside area with its many amusements.

Pot of tea 45p, cream tea £1.75
Open all year, Mon – Sat (Suns from Mar – Oct)
9am – 5pm

STOWE-BY-CHARTLEY   Staffordshire   Map 07 SJ83

Amerton Farm
Tel Weston (0889) 270294

A working farm on the Stafford/Uttoxeter road has opened its doors to the public, converting outbuildings into craft, vegetable and produce shops, developing a garden centre and encouraging visitors to view the milking parlour or follow a farm trail. A large tearoom serves its own ice cream and a wide range of home-baked pies, tarts and cakes.

Set tea £2.40
Open all year, every day,
9am – 6pm (7pm Apr – Sep)

STOW-ON-THE-WOLD   Gloucestershire   Map 04 SP12

Ann Willow Tea Room
The Square
Tel (0451) 30000

Traditional Cotswold teas are served with quiet efficiency by the owner of this bow-fronted cottage café, set beside the picturesque town square, the plain wooden furniture of its attractive interior setting off the aptly-chosen Willow Pattern crockery. Teatime treats include gâteaux, passion cake and brandy snaps as well as sandwiches, teacakes and homebaked scones.

Pot of tea 75p, set tea £2.25
Open all year, every day, 9.30am – 5.30pm (summer), 10am – 5pm (winter)

STOW-ON-THE-WOLD   Gloucestershire   Map 04 SP12

The Royalist Hotel
Digbeth Street
Tel (0451) 30670

Listed in The Guinness Book of Records as the oldest inn in England, and with beams that carbon dating has proved to be more than 1000 years old, the hotel provides both plain and cream teas, homemade fare including scones, flapjacks, shortbread, chocolate slabs and cherry butter fingers; tea is correctly made and well presented, with a limited choice of blends.

Set teas £1.40 and £1.75
Open all year, every day, 3 – 5.30pm
Bar snacks and Brasserie

STOW-ON-THE-WOLD   Gloucestershire   Map 04 SP12

Shepherd of the Hills
Sheep Street
Tel (0451) 31526

Set in one of the main thoroughfares of this attractive Cotswold town, and flanked by interesting shops, this popular, efficiently-run tearoom offers a good range of teas, snacks and light lunches, having the added advantage of being licensed. A wide variety of tea blends (including some herbal) accompanies the set cream tea or guests' choice from a selection of homemade scones, pies and cakes.

Cream tea £1.90
Open all year, every day, 10am – 9pm
Snacks and light lunches

STOW-ON-THE-WOLD   Gloucestershire   Map 04 SP12

Simpson's
Digbeth Street
Tel (0451) 30151

This traditional-style teashop stands in a terraced row of cottages stretching from the Square towards the Lower Town car park. Windsor chairs and lace-clothed tables are set against white-painted walls displaying works offered for sale by local artists. You can take either the Cotswold Cream Tea or your choice of homemade cakes, with Earl Grey or Darjeeling tea.

Pot of tea 50p – 65p, set Cotswold Cream Tea £1.90
Open all year, Mon – Sat 10am (12am Mon) – 5pm

STOW-ON-THE-WOLD   Gloucestershire   Map 04 SP12

Teapots
10 Talbot Court
Tel (0451) 32242

Housed in a listed building that once provided stabling for brewery horses, Teapots offers light lunches and afternoon teas – the Vicarage Tea being particularly popular – with homemade cakes and pastries. Pots of well-made tea are always available, even at lunch time, the choice including Earl Grey, camomile and herbal blends.

Pot of tea 65p – 75p, set teas £1.95 – £2
Open every day (except Christmas and New Year), 10am – 5.30pm
Coffee, light lunches

STRATFORD-UPON-AVON   Warwickshire   Map 04 SP25

Mistress Quickly
59–60 Henley Street
Tel (0789) 295261

Close to Shakespeare's birthplace, this is a very attractive and popular eating place which serves meals until late evening. Teacakes, scones, Danish pastries and gâteaux are all made on the premises and served by friendly staff. Cream teas are popular, especially with foreign visitors.

Pot of tea 65 – 75p, cream tea £2.45
Open all year, every day, 9am – late evening

1 3

STRATFORD-UPON-AVON   Warwickshire   Map 04 SP25

Richoux of London
Old Red Lion Court
Bridge Street
Tel (0789) 415377

Richoux has built its reputation on the wide range of pastries and gâteaux it offers. This Stratford branch is tucked away in a courtyard off the main street and is busy all day, serving a range of light meals and snacks. There is a choice of tea blends and service is prompt and efficient.

Pot of tea from £1.05, afternoon tea £3.25

STRATFORD-UPON-AVON   Warwickshire   Map 04 SP25

Shakespeare Hotel
Chapel Street
Tel (0789) 294771

The hotel, set only a short stroll from Stratford's shops and theatre, offers a formal afternoon tea of finger sandwiches, scones, toasted teacakes and fresh cream cakes, with a choice of well-made Indian, China or Earl Grey tea. A wider range of snacks and light meals is also available.

Set teas £3.25 and £4.75
Open all year, every day for teas, 3 – 5.30pm
Range of meals

SWANAGE   Dorset   Map 04 SZ07

Grand Hotel
Burlington Road
Tel (0929) 423353

A family resort hotel in an excellent cliff-top position offers scones, cakes and pastries as accompaniment to the well-made pots of Indian, Earl Grey or jasmine tea which are pleasantly served in its comfortable lounge and sun-lounge.

Set teas £3.50
Open all year, every day for teas, 3 – 5.30pm

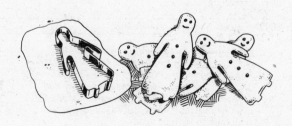

SWANSEA   West Glamorgan   Map 03 SS69

Chattery Restaurant and Coffee Shop
57 Uplands Crescent
Tel (0792) 473276

An authentic Welsh dresser and wooden farmhouse tables and chairs set the tone of this small, shopping-centre coffee shop. Here you can enjoy a cup of Assam, Darjeeling, Earl Grey or lemon tea, served with scones, teacakes and pastries; snacks and hot meals, including a vegetarian menu, are also available.

Pot of tea with teacakes
£1.25
Open all year Mon – Sat,
11am – 5.30pm (8.30pm Thur – Sat)
Snacks, hot meals

SWANSEA   West Glamorgan   Map 03 SS69

Children's World Ltd
Parc Tawe
North Dock
Quay Parade
Tel (0792) 475020

Located in a children's store at the heart of a large shopping complex near the city centre, this completely new cafeteria is light, brightly decorated and equipped with modern tubular steel and plastic furniture. Youngsters will appreciate the range of established children's favourites included among the snacks, whilst adults may enjoy a good, refreshing cup of tea with a sandwich, scone or cake.

Pot of tea with scones
£1.40
Open all year, Mon – Fri
10am – 8pm, Sat 9am –
6pm, bank holidays 10am
– 6pm

SWANSEA   West Glamorgan   Map 03 SS69

Littlewoods
St Mary's Square
Tel (0792) 469200

This self-service area, part of the main store's first floor, offsets modern furnishings with an array of potted plants. A range of meals is available, but customers requiring only a light snack may well opt for scones, gâteaux or pastries complemented by a good cup of tea – properly made and offering Earl Grey, Assam, Ceylon and Darjeeling as alternatives to the more traditional blends.

Pot of tea 48p
Open all year, Mon – Sat,
9am – 5.30pm
Coffee, lunches

SWANSEA   West Glamorgan   Map 03 SS69

Windsor Café
3 Craddock Street
Tel (0792) 652748

Clean and bright, furnished with wooden chairs, Formica-topped tables and a separate take-away area, the café serves toasted teacakes, pastries and gâteaux with a good, traditional cup of tea; ice cream and hot meals (including fish and chips) are also available.

Pot of tea with toasted
teacakes 90p
Open all year, Mon – Sat,
8.30am – 6.20pm
Hot meals (lunch, high
tea, fish and chips)

TALSARNAU   Gwynedd   Map 06 SH63

Maes-y-Neuadd Hotel
Nr Harlech
(unclassified road off B4573)
Tel (0766) 780200

This old house dates back to the 14th century and enjoys a beautiful setting in the Welsh hills, looking out to the sea. Afternoon tea is served in the attractive, comfortable lounge, and an excellent array of homemade scones, cakes and biscuits, including local specialities such as bara brith, is laid out on the sideboard for you to help yourself. Tea, in a choice of several blends, is served in china pots by the young and friendly staff.

Pot of tea £1
Open all year, every day, 3.30 – 5.30pm

1   2   3

TARPORLEY   Cheshire   Map 07 SJ56

Feathers Coffee Shop
105 High Street
Tel (082 93) 2812

A small coffee shop specialising in homemade cakes, scones, quiches and such like, situated on the first floor of a ladies' fashion shop at the southern end of the High Street.

Pot of tea 50p, cream tea 95p
Open all year, Mon – Sat, 9.30am – 5pm

1   3

TAUNTON   Somerset   Map 03 ST22

Coffee & Cream
6–8 Crown Walk
Tel (0823) 283764

A modern, glass-fronted building with a quarry-tiled and carpeted floor, fixed tables and benches or chairs, floral drapes, dried flowers and a long buffet-style service counter. Home-baked scones, cakes and gâteaux are available with bought-in Danish pastries.

Cup of tea 48p
Open all year, Mon – Sat, 8.30am – 5pm

TAUNTON   Somerset   Map 03 ST22

Riverside Restaurant
Riverside Place
St James Street
Tel (0823) 251761

Set in a small courtyard beside the River Tone, the restaurant has a modern décor with festoon blinds, formica-topped tables and aluminium framed chairs. There is an extensive buffet counter serving cream teas, sandwiches, salads, soup and homemade cakes, gâteaux, pastries and biscuits.

Cup of tea 45p, set tea £1.75
Open all year, Mon – Sat, 9am – 5.30pm

TAUNTON   Somerset   Map 03 ST22

Victorian Rooms
County Hotel
East Street
Tel (0823) 337651

An attractive split-level room with a bow window facing the main shopping street and many pictures and plants. There are wooden topped tables and wicker-backed chairs. Crumpets, sweet biscuits, teacakes, scones and Danish pastries from the local baker are served with a choice of tea blends. Good china pots are used with a pleasing mixture of crockery.

Cup of tea 90p, cream tea £2.80
Open all year, Mon – Sat, 9.30am – 5pm

1 2 3

TAVISTOCK   Devon   Map 02 SX47

The Coffee Mill
44 Brook Street
Tel (0822) 612092

You will easily find this Georgian-fronted shop in the town's main street. Inside, the wood-panelled walls, plants, pictures and brown earthenware crockery create a pleasant atmosphere, and Mr Martindale and his staff will make you very welcome. There are usually at least 30 different cakes to tempt you, virtually all of them homemade, and the excellent cheesecakes are renowned in the locality. Blackcurrant and almond slice, marmalade cake and pear and ginger cake are just some of the other goodies on offer. The choice of freshly made teas is also excellent.

Pot of tea 52p, cream tea £1.98
Open all year, Mon – Sat 9.30am – 5.30pm, Sun 12 noon – 5pm (in summer open until 8pm)
Snacks and light meals also served

1 3

TAYNUILT   Strathclyde   *Argyllshire*   Map 10 NN03

**Shore Cottage
Tearoom**
Tel (08662) 654

Shore Cottage stands beside Loch Etive, in the shadow of Ben Cruachan. The countryside round about is superb and a paradise for walkers. Lilly NcNaught, the owner, draws customers from far and wide to sample her excellent baking, which she does every day, so the selection of tempting sponges, cakes and pastries is constantly varied. Scones, with her homemade rhubarb and orange jam, are always popular and the fruit slice is especially to be recommended. The tea, served in bone-china cups, is also delicious and there is a choice of blends. Craftware and paintings are on sale in the tearooms. No smoking is permitted.

Pot of tea from 40p, cakes from 40p
Open Easter – mid Oct, every day except Wed, 10am – 6pm

TEIGNMOUTH   Devon   Map 03 SX97

Beachcomber
The Promenade
Tel (0626) 778909

This coastal tearoom, in a central position on the promenade, has a modernised interior with good pine tables and chairs. A choice of teas is available and a range of homemade cakes, scones, biscuits and desserts is served by uniformed staff. There are no private toilets but public facilities are nearby.

Devon cream tea £1.75
Open all year, every day, 10am – 8pm (6pm in winter)
Lunches

TENBY   Dyfed   Map 02 SN10

Charny's Licensed Restaurant
High Street

A friendly restaurant in the centre of this most attractive seaside resort, it is easy to find, being situated almost opposite the church. A full range of hot meals is served and teacakes, cream teas and doughnuts are also available in the afternoons to accompany a good pot of tea.

Tea 40p, cream teas £1
Open all year, Mon – Sat
Hot meals

TETBURY   Gloucestershire   Map 03 ST89

The Close Hotel
Tel (0666) 52272

The Close Hotel dates back 400 years and is built on the site of a ruined monastery. Although right in the centre of this charming old Cotswold town, it has all the tranquillity and atmosphere of a country-house hotel. The traditional afternoon tea is a substantial feast of dainties, all homemade in the hotel and you can enjoy your cream tea, your chocolate and banana cake with vanilla ice-cream or your apple and poppy seed cake in the lounge, under the elegant domed ceiling of the withdrawing room, or in the hotel gardens.

Tea and cake £1.70, cream tea £2.75
Open May – Sep, every day, 3 – 5.30pm
[1] [2] [3]

TETBURY   Gloucestershire   Map 03 ST89

Two Toads
19 Church Street
Tel (0666) 53696

This family-run, town-centre restaurant has a tongue twister of a name, but thankfully only the first two words form the shop title: 'Two toads totally tired tried to trot to Tetbury'. There is a wide-ranging snack and lunch menu, and for tea, homemade cakes, scones, teacakes and doughnuts. A choice of tea blends is offered, including herbal.

Pot of tea from 40p, cream tea £1.50
Open all year, Tue – Sun, 9am – 5.30pm, teas served 2 – 5.30pm
Lunches

TEWKESBURY   Gloucestershire   Map 03 SO83

Abbey Tearooms
59 Church Street
Tel (0684) 292215

About 450 years old, these tearooms are full of olde worlde charm with exposed beams, an open fireplace and polished wood tables and chairs. Light lunches are available, but it is the range of homemade cakes and puddings, traditional cream teas and gâteaux that have made the tearooms popular. A choice of teas is offered. Smoking is not permitted.

Pot of tea 45p – 50p
Open early Mar – mid Nov, Wed – Mon, 10.30am – 5.30pm
Lunches

THORNHAM MAGNA   Suffolk   Map 05 TM17

Red House Forge Tearooms
Redhouse Yard
Tel Mellis (037 983) 794

In a really lovely setting, the teashop is found in the old forge, up a few steps, where there are pretty, clothed tables, brightly coloured chairs, bare floorboards and wicker mats. There is also a pottery and a silk-screen printers in the yard, and a park with Ramblers walks. There are assorted wholesome homemade cakes and a range of tea blends. Smoking is not permitted.

Pot of tea 45p
Open Mar – Dec, every day, 10.30am – 5.30pm

TIVERTON   Devon   Map 03 SS91

Carwardine's
1 Phoenix Lane
Tel (0884) 254687

A town-centre coffee/tea house and restaurant with comfortable booth seating. Meals and snacks are served all day from breakfast to afternoon tea. A good range of homemade pastries and desserts is available with various blends of good, large-leaf teas and freshly roasted coffees. There is also a selection of ice creams. A retail section sells speciality teas and freshly ground coffee.

Pot of tea 70p, cakes from 70p (min charge £1)
Open all year, every day, 8.30am – 6pm (8pm summer) Mon – Sat, 10am – 5pm Sun
Breakfast, lunch

TOTNES   Devon   Map 03 SX86

Anne of Cleves
56 Fore Street
Tel (0803) 863186

The main street of this picturesque old town climbs steeply uphill, and this tearoom is a very popular resting place. Making the range of about 50 assorted cakes, pastries, scones and other temptations keeps two chefs on the go all day. As everywhere in this part of the country, cream teas are favourites, but there are also excellent teacakes, crumpets and muffins to precede your plate of gâteaux. The tea blends are also very good and there is a choice of well-made Indian, lemon, Earl Grey or herbal infusions.

Devonshire cream tea £2.10, pot of tea from 50p, gâteaux from £1
Open all year, every day, 9am – 5.30pm

TREFRIW   Gwynedd   Map 06 SH76

Trefriw Wells Spa Teahouse
(on B5106 at entrance of Roman Spa Cave of Wells)
Tel (0492) 640057

In Victorian times this attractive café was the Pump Room Bathhouse, and you can still buy bottles of the chalybeate spa water in the adjoining shop. A selection of homemade scones, teacakes and cakes is on offer and there is a choice of blends of tea on request.

Pot of tea 40p, cream tea £1.15
Open Feb – Nov, every day, 10am – 5.30pm
Light lunches and snacks also served

TUNBRIDGE WELLS (ROYAL)   Kent   Map 05 TQ53

Chocolate Centre
70 Camden Road
Tel (0892) 31683

As might be expected from the name, this delightful shop, with a restaurant at the rear, makes and sells the most delicious chocolates. Its restaurant is most attractive and displays its appealing, homemade cakes and gâteaux on a trolley, so that you can inspect the day's range of delicacies with ease. Among the specialities which may tempt you are Normandy apple tart, gypsy tart, butter creams and Wellington squares. There is a choice of blends of tea or herbal infusions and everything is nicely served. No smoking is permitted.

Pot of tea £1.00, cream tea £2.00
Open all year, Mon – Sat, 9am – 5.30pm

TUNBRIDGE WELLS (ROYAL)   Kent   Map 05 TQ53

Importers Tea and Coffee House
22 Monson Road
Tel (0892) 27567

An attractive establishment, with plain wooden tables and chairs, to the rear of a shop selling speciality teas and freshly roasted coffees. The cake trolley is tempting, displaying homebaked scones and apple pies as well as gâteaux and cheesecakes. A choice of teas is offered.

Pot of tea 55p, cream tea £1.65
Open all year, Mon – Sat, 9am – 5pm
1   3

TUNBRIDGE WELLS (ROYAL)   Kent   Map 05 TQ53

Rupert's High Street Tel (0892) 511045	An attractive multi-purpose bar-café, light and airy with plants and a walled garden. Sandwiches, filled rolls, scones, gâteaux and Danish pastries are served, and a range of Indian and China tea blends.	Pot of tea 90p, Kentish cream tea £2.35 Open all year, Mon – Sat, 10am – 4.30pm ⊡1 ⊡2 ⊡3

TURNBERRY   Strathclyde   *Ayrshire*   Map 10 NS20

The Turnberry Hotel Tel (0655) 31000	This high-quality hotel overlooking the Firth of Clyde and the massive rock of Ailsa Craig is famed for its championship golf courses and for its traditional Scottish hospitality. Afternoon tea is served in the comfortable Ailsa Lounge in an atmosphere of elegance and refinement reminiscent of days gone by. There is an excellent selection of sandwiches, scones, pancakes, crumpets, cakes and pastries, all freshly made. The fine bone china is in keeping with the surroundings and there is a choice of three China teas, as well as Indian, Ceylon, and Earl Grey.	Full afternoon tea £6.25, pot of tea £1.65, cakes £1.65 Open all year, every day, 2.30 – 5pm ⊡1 ⊡2 ⊡3

TWIGWORTH   Gloucestershire   Map 03 SO82

Wooden Spoon Wallsworth Hall Tel (0452) 731422	Wallsworth Hall is the international centre for wildlife art. The Wooden Spoon is also open to non-visitors and snacks and meals are available throughout the day. There is a wide range of homebaking on offer, including wholefood items. Good tea nicely served and a choice of blends is available. Smoking is not permitted.	Tea £1.80 Open all year, Tue – Sun, 10am – 5pm Lunches

---

TY NANT   Clwyd   Map 06 SJ15

Bronnant Teashop Corwen Tel (049 081) 344	A quaint white-painted gift and teashop on the busy A494. Home-cooked cakes and pastries, savoury snacks and breakfasts are available in the high season. A variety of tea blends is offered, and a choice of whole or skimmed milk for the health-conscious.	Pot of tea 50p – 75p, cream tea £1.90 Open Mar – Oct, every day in high season, 10am – 6pm (8am – 10pm high season)

ULLAPOOL   Highland   *Ross and Cromarty*   Map 14 NH19

Ceilidh Place Hotel
West Argyle Street
Tel (0854) 2103

A popular, comfortable tourist hotel. The self-service coffee shop has an informal atmosphere and is full of character with rough cast and timber walls, a stone floor with bright rugs and a log burner when required. Some of the seating is made from old church pews. Bread, scones and cakes are all homebaked and there is a wide selection of speciality leaf teas.

Open mid Jan – Dec, every day, 10am – 6pm winter, 10am – 6pm summer
[1] [2] [3]

ULVERSTON   Cumbria   Map 07 SD27

The Peppermill
64 Market Street
Tel (0229) 57564

This small, popular restaurant has a cottage feel to it, with exposed beams, white walls, red-clothed tables and flower paintings. The attractive garden is also used in summer. As well as light meals, a selection of scones, teabreads, meringues and lovely sweets like banana toffee pie are served in the afternoons. A choice of tea blends is offered.

Pot of tea 45p
Open all year, Mon – Sat, 9.15am – 5.15pm
Lunch
[1] [3]

UPPER DEAL   Kent   Map 05 TR35

The Tea Gardens
224 London Road
Tel (0304) 375270

An attractive tearoom, fully carpeted with polished cottage tables, wooden chairs and pot plants. There is a small terrace outside with tables and umbrellas. The menu offers a selection of snacks, light refreshments and substantial roasts. A choice of tea blends is offered, and cakes, fruit pies and teabreads are available.

Pot of tea 60p
Open all year, Tue – Sun (Thu half day), 11am – 6.30pm
Lunches

UPPINGHAM   Leicestershire   Map 04 SP89

Baines Tea Room
High Street West
Tel (0572) 823317

Part of a butcher's and baker's business, housed in 17th-century premises in the centre of this historic Rutland town, the tearoom has simple but quaint cottage-style furniture with lace table cloths, napkins and good china. A wide range of delectable homemade cakes, teabreads and sandwiches are offered as well as light meals. A selection of tea blends, including herbal, is available. Smoking is not permitted.

Pot of tea 45p, cream tea £1.25
Open all year, Mon – Sat (ex Mon and Thu pm in winter), 9am – 5pm
Lunches

UPTON ST LEONARDS   Gloucestershire   Map 03 SO81

Hatton Court Hotel
Upton Hill
Tel (0452) 617412

Set in lovely countryside just outside Gloucester, Hatton Court is surrounded by parkland and gardens. Afternoon tea is served in the comfortable lounge, and all the produce is freshly baked by the hotel. There is a choice of blends of tea.

Pot of tea £1.25, cream tea £2.75, afternoon tea £4.25
Open all year, every day, 3 – 5.30pm

1   2   3

UWCHMYNYDD   Gwynedd   Map 06 SC12

Pen Bryn Bach
Aberdaron
Tel (075 886) 216

A pleasant little café-tearoom situated near the end of the Lleyn Peninsula in a lovely rural setting. Split-level, with pretty green checked cloths on its tables and good crockery, the room is decorated with pictures and dried flowers, and there is piped music. A good selection of homemade cakes is offered and full meals are also available.

Pot of tea 65p
Open Easter – Sep, every day, 10am – 10pm
Lunch, dinner

WALLINGFORD   Oxfordshire   Map 04 SU68

George Hotel
66 High Street
Tel (0491) 36665

A timbered Tudor Inn with traditional public rooms and a pleasant secluded courtyard and terrace. Sandwiches, scones, teacakes and pastries are served with a choice of tea blends.

Full cream tea £4.50
Open all year, every day, 10am – 4.30pm

1   2   3

WARE   Hertfordshire   Map 05 TL31

Van Hage's Coffee Shop
Van Hage's Garden Centre
Amwell Hill
Great Amwell
Tel (0920) 870811

Located within the garden centre, the self-service coffee shop is a wooden building with red and white furnishings giving a bright and cheerful effect. A good selection of homemade cakes, scones, shortbread, sponges and flapjacks are offered with a choice of tea blends. Smoking is not permitted.

Tea 40p
Open all year, (except Christmas week), every day, 10am – 5pm

1   3   ⅍

WAREHAM   Dorset   Map 03 SY98

Priory Hotel
Church Green
Tel (09295) 2772

In a tranquil setting next to the church, with two acres of garden running down to the river, the converted 16th-century priory offers gracious, comfortably appointed lounges where tea is served. Scones, cakes, gâteaux, sandwiches and cream teas are available with a choice of good leaf-tea blends and herbal infusions.

Set tea £3.90
Open all year, every day, tea served 3pm – 5pm

1   2   3

WATERMILLOCK   Cumbria   Map 12 NY42

Leeming House
Ullswater
Tel (08536) 622

A country-house hotel on the shores of Lake Ullswater set in 20 acres of landscaped gardens and natural woodland. Tea is served in peaceful, elegant lounges with an open log fire and fine views. Tea and biscuits are available, or a full tea comprising fresh sandwiches, scones, cakes and biscuits. A choice of leaf teas is offered, properly made and served, with Wedgwood china cups.

Tea and biscuits £1.20, full tea £4.75
Open all year, every day, morning coffee 10.30am – noon, afternoon tea 3 – 5pm

1 2 3

WELLS   Somerset   Map 03 ST54

The Cloister Restaurant
Wells Cathedral
Tel (0749) 76543

Situated in the west cloister of this magnificent Cathedral, the Cloister Restaurant is an unusual setting for afternoon tea. Several tea varieties, including herbal, are offered and the food is all homemade with some wholefood items. There are 'healthy' cakes, cream cakes and sponges. Morning coffee and lunches are also served. Smoking is not permitted.

Pot of tea 40p, cakes 25p – 65p
Open all year, (except Christmas), Mon – Sat, 10am – 5pm, Sun 2 – 5pm
Lunches

WELLS   Somerset   Map 03 ST54

The Good Earth
4 Priory Road
Tel (0749) 78600

This is a licensed vegetarian restaurant and wholefood store. The restaurant comprises several pine-floored rooms plus the garden courtyard. Everything is homemade with natural, unrefined ingredients. Moist cakes include carrot cake and traditional Somerset dappy. A selection of teas is available including herb teas. A blackboard menu offers a range of lunch-time dishes.

Pot of tea 50p, cakes 50p
Open all year, Mon – Sat, 9.30am – 5.30pm
Lunches (dish of the day £1.65)

1 2

WELLS-NEXT-THE-SEA   Norfolk   Map 09 TF94

Corner House Restaurant and Tearoom
Staithe Street
Tel Fakenham (0328) 711317

A fully restored tearoom and restaurant away from the busy sea front but close to the shops. It has a cottage-style interior with pretty embroidered tablecloths, lace curtains and quality china. A warm, cheery welcome, a good cup of tea and a range of scones, pastries and fruit pies are offered. A choice of tea blends, including fruit teas, is available.

Pot of tea 50p – 75p
Open all year, every day, in summer, closed Mon and Thu winter, 10.30am – 5pm

1

WELSHPOOL   Powys   Map 07 SJ20

The Inglenook Teashop Union Street Tel (0938) 5188	A cottage-style teashop with wooden tables and farmhouse chairs. A small range of Welsh crafts is on display and for sale. Pastries, scones and pies, all homemade, are available with some hot snacks as well. A choice of tea blends is offered.	Tea 50p, cream tea £1.25 Open all year, Mon, Fri and Sat 9am – 5pm; Tue, Wed and Thu 9.30 – 5pm

---

WELSHPOOL   Powys   Map 07 SJ20

National Milk Bar 21 Church Street Tel (0938) 2470	A popular rendezvous for local youngsters, this is a café-style operation in the centre of town, with formica tables and plastic seating. Some hot snacks are served and cream cakes and scones.	Tea and scones £1.40 Open all year, every day, 8am – 8pm

---

WETHERBY   West Yorkshire   Map 08 SE44

Le Bon Appetit 12 Bank Street Tel (0937) 580027	The proprietors of this small, quaint teashop take great pride in their menu which boasts all homemade food for morning coffee, light lunch and afternoon tea. Homemade croissants, cakes and delicious gâteaux are served, with a choice of tea blends, by courteous staff.	Teas £1.50 – £2 Open all year, Mon – Sat, 9.30am – 4.30pm (occasionally 8pm)

WETHERBY   West Yorkshire   Map 08 SE44

Rooftops Scandanavian Kitchen 9 The Shambles Tel (0937) 65560	In the town centre, on the first floor above the shopping area, this is an attractive and inviting little restaurant with its white and green décor. The theme is Scandanavian, with a mouthwatering array of pastries and unusual cakes and gâteaux. There are superb open sandwiches with the most interesting fillings. A choice of teas is served in china teapots. No smoking at lunchtime.	Open all year, Mon – Sat, 9.30am – 4.30pm

---

WHITEHOUSE   Strathclyde   *Argyllshire*   Map 10 NR86

Old School Tearoom Tel (088073) 215	A homely village tearoom with timber-clad walls and varnished wood floor. A coal fire burns on cooler days and there are outside tables for the better weather. Savoury items feature local produce such as venison, salmon and crab and the cake trolley is laden with tempting homemade cakes and pastries. Our inspector particularly recommends the deep rum and choc cheesecake. A choice of tea blends is available.	Pot of tea 40p – 50p Open Easter – Oct, Wed – Mon, 10.30am – 6pm

WHITMORE   Staffordshire   Map 07 SK84

Whitmore Gallery and Tea Rooms
Keele Road
Tel (0782) 680879

Originally built as a public house, this 17th-century cottage was a saddlery until its recent transformation. Knitwear, pottery and paintings are on sale while speciality teas are served with good homemade cakes. Lunches are served, and vegetarians well catered for. The menu offers two local dishes: oatcakes, and lobby, a filling soup.

Scone, jam and cream from 60p
Open all year, every day, 10am – 6pm
Lunches
[1] [3]

WIGHT, ISLE OF   Gurnard   Map 04 SZ59

Bowspit Teashop
21 Princes Esplanade
Tel (0983) 291933

A small bungalow teashop facing the sea, serving farmers' lunches, snacks, homemade pies, quiches, freshly made sandwiches, cream teas and ice cream. Children and pets are particularly welcome. No smoking is requested.

Set tea £1.75
Open Easter – Nov, Tue – Sun and bank holidays, 10.30am – 5pm

WIMBORNE MINSTER   Dorset   Map 04 SZ09

Kings Head
The Square
Tel (0202) 880101

A country-town hotel with good lounge facilities, modern and comfortable. Scones, cakes, sponges and sandwiches are served with a choice of Earl Grey or China tea.

Open all year, every day, tea served, 3 – 5.30pm
[1] [2] [3]

WIMBORNE MINSTER   Dorset   Map 04 SZ09

Quinney's
26 Westborough
Tel (0202) 883518

A small town-centre restaurant on two floors serving morning coffee, lunch and afternoon tea with a good selection of homemade cakes. A choice of tea blends is offered.

Cream tea £1.85
Open all year, Tue – Sat, 9.15am – 5.15pm
Lunch

WINCHCOMBE   Gloucestershire   Map 03 SO92

Lady Jane's Tea Shop
7 Hailes Street
Tel (0242) 603578

A light, airy dining room with pretty tablecloths, china and fresh carnations. There are spindle-back chairs and attractive shell lightshades. A comprehensive menu is served, but teas are a speciality, with a good range of homemade cakes, meringue pies and cheesecakes. There are cream teas, a 'winter warmer' with hot crumpets, and a children's tea with honey sandwiches.

Teas £1.80 – £2.30
Open all year, every day, 10am – 6pm

WINCHELSEA   East Sussex   Map 05 TV92

Finches
12 High Street
Tel (0747) 226284

Conveniently situated next to the village post office, this period cottage restaurant features a varied choice of scones, crumpets, toasted teacakes and set cream tea; also a wide selection of homemade cakes, pastries and gâteaux. Freshly made loose leaf tea is served, and a choice of blends is available.

Set tea £1.80
Open Jan – Dec, every day,
9.30am – 6pm
[1] [2] [3]

WINCHESTER   Hampshire   Map 04 SU42

**Lainston House
Hotel**
Sparsholt (outside
Winchester off A272)
Tel (0962) 63588

Set in rolling parkland and well kept gardens, Lainston House dates back to the era of William and Mary and offers a most elegant, peaceful setting for a traditional afternoon tea, which may be served either in the beautifully furnished drawing room or in the gardens. Sandwiches, scones and gâteaux are all freshly made by the hotel kitchens, which have a high reputation for their cooking, and there is a good choice of blends of tea, all served by very friendly, cheerful staff.

Traditional afternoon tea
£5.75
Open every day, 3 – 6pm
[1] [2] [3] [&]

WINCHESTER   Hampshire   Map 04 SU42

Royal Hotel
St Peter Street
Tel (0962) 840840

This former convent is centrally situated. It has well tended gardens and a stylish garden lounge where Ceylon and China teas are served with sandwiches, biscuits, fruitcake or Danish pastry. Daily papers are available.

Pot of tea 90p
Open all year, every day,
10am – noon and 3 – 6pm
[1] [3]

WINDERMERE   Cumbria   Map 07 SD49

Apple Cottage
21 Victoria Street
Tel (09662) 5234

A smart little teashop with a country Victorian feel to it. Charmingly decorated, with a wrought iron spiral staircase from first to second floor. The atmosphere is relaxed but civilised. Light meals are served at lunch time, and a range of quality homebaked scones, biscuits and teabreads is displayed on a dresser. A choice of tea blends is available. Smoking is not permitted.

Pot of tea 50p – 60p
Open all year, Mon –
Sat, 10am – 5pm.
Lunches

WINDERMERE   Cumbria   Map 07 SD49

Miller Howe Hotel
Rayrigg Road
Tel (09662) 4536

John Tovey has established an international
reputation for this first-class Lakeland hotel. From the
lounges where tea is served there are magnificent
views across the lake to the Cumbrian fells beyond, a
prospect to stimulate your appetite for the delectable
cakes and pastries you are about to sample. The full
afternoon tea comprises shortbread, scones with
cream and fresh fruit, followed perhaps by very rich
chocolate cake or a fresh fruit tart, with crème
patissière. All this, and the good strong tea, is
beautifully served in Wedgwood bone china.

Set afternoon tea £4.50
Open all year, every day,
3 – 5pm
[1] [2] [3]

WINDERMERE   Cumbria   Map 07 SD49

Miller Howe Kaff at
Lakeland Plastics
Station Precinct
Tel (09662) 6732

A small busy café which is part of the Lakeland Plastics
Shop. Modern, light and bright but trying to be stylish.
Exceptionally popular at lunch time as an eating
place. Leaf tea is served in a silver pot with
Wedgwood china. A small choice of homemade cakes
and scones is available. Smoking is not permitted.

Pot of tea 60p
Open all year, Mon –
Sat, 9.30am – 4.30pm
Lunches
[&]

WINDERMERE   Cumbria   Map 07 SD49

Tea Shoppe
Field House
Bowness-on-
Windermere
Tel (09662) 2476

A pleasant basement tearoom overlooking a small
garden close to the centre of town. Part of a
guesthouse with self-catering units, the Tea Shoppe
also sells a range of gifts. Freshly made sandwiches
are served with homemade cakes and scones with
generous portions of cream. A range of speciality teas
is available. Smoking is not permitted.

Pot of tea 45p
Open all year, Fri –
Wed, 10am – 5.30pm

WINDSOR   Berkshire   Map 04 SU97

The Courtyard
8 King George V Place
Tel (0753) 858338

A small teashop located in a busy courtyard close to the river, the castle and the town centre. A choice of teas is offered with sandwiches, salads, pastries, croissants and gâteaux.

Pot of tea 65p-75p, English cream tea £2.10
Open Jan – Dec (except Christmas), every day, 11.30am – 5pm (6pm weekends)

WINDSOR   Berkshire   Map 04 SU97

The Hideaway
Sir Christopher Wren's
House Hotel
12 Thames Street
Tel (0753) 842186

A pleasant restaurant with exposed brick walls, modern prints and attractive drapes. A selection of speciality teas is served with scones, cakes, Danish pastries and gâteaux.

Pot of tea 85p, cream tea £3.75
Open Jan – Dec, every day, 10am – 11pm
[1] [2] [3]

WOODBRIDGE   Suffolk   Map 05 TM24

Mrs Pipers
65 The Thoroughfare
Tel (0394) 355633

A blue-painted teashop in the middle of the village, the interior of this teashop is decorated in blue and white to match, with exposed beams, Welsh dresser, white chairs and pretty tablecloths. There are pictures for sale and attractive displays of homemade cakes and sweets. Light snacks are served, and afternoon tea comprising cucumber sandwiches, fruit scone, cream and jam. A choice of teas is offered.

Pot of tea 55p, afternoon tea £2.25, children's tea £1.40
Open Jan – Dec, Tue – Sun, 9.45am – 5.15pm
Tue, Thu and Fri, 9.45am – 2.15pm Wed, 9.30am – 5.30pm Sat, 11am – 5pm Sun

---

WOODSTOCK   Oxfordshire   Map 04 SP41

The Blenheim
Tel (0993) 811467

Named after the Blenheim Orange apple tree, the first of which was grown in Woodstock. This traditional country tearoom, known especially for its cream teas, is located by the entrance to Blenheim Palace and is popular with tourists and Oxford undergraduates alike. An extensive range of speciality teas is served with a good selection of cakes.

Pot of tea 80p, set tea £2.20
Open Jan – Dec, every day (except Mon Oct – Mar), 10am – 5pm (10.30am – 5.30pm winter)

WORCESTER   Worcestershire   Map 03 SO85

The Commandery
Sidbury
Tel (0905) 358097

Its canalside setting adds to the charm of this pleasant tearoom, housed next to a museum in an old timber-framed building with Civil War connections – hence the name. Good gâteaux and cream teas are served by friendly staff.

Cream tea £1.75
Open every day, Mon – Sat 10.30am – 5pm, Sun 2 – 5pm
Light meals also served
[4]

WORCESTER   Worcestershire   Map 03 SO85

The Shepherd's Purse
7 Severn Street
Tel (0905) 726770

This pretty cottage-style tearoom was once a fisherman's inn. It stands opposite the Royal Worcester Spode factory and is close to the cathedral and city centre. Good homemade scones, cakes and gâteaux are served by friendly staff and there is a choice of teas.

Pot of tea 50p
Open all year, Mon – Sat, 10.30am – 5.30pm
Other light meals also served

WORTHING   West Sussex   Map 04 TQ10

Oojies Coffee Shop
Chatsworth Hotel
18A Marine Parade
Tel (0903) 203589

Fine teas and coffees are served in comfortable surroundings with Cornish cream teas or a selection from the pâtisseries. Daily 'homecooked specials' are available, also fresh fish and seafood dishes.

Open all year, Tue – Sun, 10am – 5pm Tue – Sat, 11am – 5pm Sun Lunch

WROXHAM   Norfolk   Map 09 TG31

Hotel Wroxham
Broad Centre
Tel (0603) 782061

A popular meeting place in the town, the servery is an integral part of the hotel. Large windows overlook the river, or one can sit out in the large riverside patio area. There is a mouthwatering display of cakes and pastries from the hotel kitchen and hot food is also served.

Cream tea £1.25
Open all year, every day, 10am – 9pm
Hot meals
[1] [2] [3] [&]

WROXHAM   Norfolk   Map 09 TG31

Ye Olde Mill Tea Shoppe
The Bridge
Tel (0603) 783744

A small friendly self-service café on the banks of the river offering a selection of light snacks and teas all day. Cakes and pastries are produced by a local baker. Seating is available indoors and out.

Teas £1.05
Open mid Feb – mid Jan, Mon – Sat 9am – 4pm winter, every day Easter – Oct 8am – 5.30pm
Light snacks

YARM   Cleveland   Map 08 N241

The Coffee Shop
44 High Street
Tel (0642) 790000

Situated over the Strickland and Holt department store in the main street of this attractive little town, stripped pine furniture gives a country feel to the Coffee Shop. All the food is homemade from natural ingredients. Breakfast and light lunches are served as well as scones, biscuits and a range of puddings and ice creams. A choice of five teas is offered.

Pot of tea 59p
Open all year, Mon – Sat, 9am – 5pm
Breakfast, lunch

YEOVIL   Somerset   Map 03 ST51

Denners
High Street
Tel (0935) 74444

A modern coffee/teashop on the third floor of Denners department store. The restaurant is glass-fronted with functional but comfortable furnishings. Food is displayed on a long service counter: homemade cakes and scones are supplemented by commercially made biscuits and gâteaux. Hot dishes are also served with snacks such as toasted sandwiches for a light lunch.

Cup of tea 45p
Open all year, Mon –
Sat, 9.30am – 5.30pm
Lunch

YORK   North Yorkshire   Map 08 SE65

Betty's Café Tea Rooms
6–8 St Helen's Square
Tel (0904) 659142

Just a short walk from York Minster, Betty's is a branch of the renowned Harrogate tearooms founded in 1919 by a Swiss confectioner who settled there. The identity of 'Betty' herself is a House secret. The tearooms serve a huge array of delectable baking, made every day in the café's Harrogate bakery, combining traditional Yorkshire recipes with Continental pâtisseries to please every taste. The range of blends of tea is excellent and the service maintains the highest traditional standards. There are often queues of would-be customers. See also entries for Harrogate, Ilkley and Northallerton.

Afternoon tea £2.90
Open every day, 9am –
9pm
Other meals also
served

[1] [2] [3]

YORK   North Yorkshire   Map 08 SE65

York Crest Hotel
Clifford Tower
Tower Street
Tel (0904) 648111

The ideal stopping place for visitors exploring the historic features of the city. Service is available in the cosy lounge or attractive cocktail area. Traditional afternoon tea with home-baked scones, cream and strawberry jam, sandwiches and a selection of cakes and pastries is served by courteous staff. A choice of tea blends is offered.

Afternoon tea £3.75
Open Jan – Dec, every day,
9.30am – 5.30pm

[1] [2] [3] [&]

BAKEWELL
BYWAYS

WATER LANE   BAKEWELL   DERBYSHIRE – Telephone: 0629 812807

Breakfast – Morning Coffee – Lunch – Afternoon Tea – High Tea – Full menu
available all day – All freshly prepared to order – Home-made Bakewell Tart, Cakes
and Pastries – Children, Hikers, back packers all welcome

Billesley Manor
S T R A T F O R D · U P O N · A V O N

Billesley, Alcester,
Warwickshire B49 6NF.
Telephone: 0789-400888.
Telex: 312599. Fax: (0789) 764145

Billesley Manor, set in 11 acres of parkland and formal gardens, just three miles from Stratford on Avon, provides an idyllic setting. Enjoy a leisurely afternoon in the beautiful Lounges
with log fires, on the Terrace throughout the summer, or perhaps by the superb indoor heated swimming pool. The menu includes an imaginative selection of sandwiches, teacakes,
crumpets and homemade biscuits.

Romany Tea Rooms

Morning coffees, afternoon teas,
light lunches. All our produce is
home-made with the very best of ingredients.
OPEN 7 DAYS A WEEK – 10 TILL 5PM
Children's play area and video cinema.
Whilst visiting us, why not look round our craft and leisure shop?
HARRINGTONS CARAVAN AND LEISURE WORLD
AT CHESTER ROAD, DELAMERE FOREST, NEAR NORTHWICH. TEL: 0606 882032.

Egon Ronay Starred

The Tea Shoppe
3, High Street, Dunster, Somerset
15th Century Cottage Tea Rooms

Coffee, Cakes, Cream Teas
Light Lunches [Licensed]
Home Baking from the Tea Shoppe Kitchen

Norman & Pam Goldsack   Tel: Dunster 821304

Readers' Recommendations

We realise that, as there are so many lovely places throughout the country to stop for tea, we may not have listed your own favourite, so we would be very grateful if you could let us know about any teashop, restaurant or hotel where you have enjoyed a particularly good afternoon tea.

We should also be interested to hear any comments you have on any of the places that we do list.

Please send your report forms, which will of course be treated in confidence, to:

The Automobile Association

Guidebook Publications Unit,

Fanum House,

Basingstoke,

Hants. RG21 2EA.

YOUR NAME_____

ADDRESS_____

_____

_____

AA MEMBERSHIP NUMBER (IF ANY)_____

IS THE ESTABLISHMENT LISTED IN LET'S STOP FOR TEA'?   YES ☐   NO ☐

NAME OF ESTABLISHMENT:_____

ADDRESS:_____

_____

_____

YOUR COMMENTS:_____

_____

_____

_____

_____

_____

_____

_____

IS THE ESTABLISHMENT LISTED IN LET'S STOP FOR TEA'?　　　　　YES ☐　　NO ☐

NAME OF ESTABLISHMENT:＿＿＿＿＿＿＿＿＿＿＿＿＿＿＿＿＿＿＿＿＿＿＿

ADDRESS:＿＿＿＿＿＿＿＿＿＿＿＿＿＿＿＿＿＿＿＿＿＿＿＿＿＿＿＿＿＿＿

＿＿＿＿＿＿＿＿＿＿＿＿＿＿＿＿＿＿＿＿＿＿＿＿＿＿＿＿＿＿＿＿＿＿＿＿

＿＿＿＿＿＿＿＿＿＿＿＿＿＿＿＿＿＿＿＿＿＿＿＿＿＿＿＿＿＿＿＿＿＿＿＿

YOUR COMMENTS:＿＿＿＿＿＿＿＿＿＿＿＿＿＿＿＿＿＿＿＿＿＿＿＿＿＿＿

＿＿＿＿＿＿＿＿＿＿＿＿＿＿＿＿＿＿＿＿＿＿＿＿＿＿＿＿＿＿＿＿＿＿＿＿

＿＿＿＿＿＿＿＿＿＿＿＿＿＿＿＿＿＿＿＿＿＿＿＿＿＿＿＿＿＿＿＿＿＿＿＿

＿＿＿＿＿＿＿＿＿＿＿＿＿＿＿＿＿＿＿＿＿＿＿＿＿＿＿＿＿＿＿＿＿＿＿＿

＿＿＿＿＿＿＿＿＿＿＿＿＿＿＿＿＿＿＿＿＿＿＿＿＿＿＿＿＿＿＿＿＿＿＿＿

＿＿＿＿＿＿＿＿＿＿＿＿＿＿＿＿＿＿＿＿＿＿＿＿＿＿＿＿＿＿＿＿＿＿＿＿

＿＿＿＿＿＿＿＿＿＿＿＿＿＿＿＿＿＿＿＿＿＿＿＿＿＿＿＿＿＿＿＿＿＿＿＿

＿＿＿＿＿＿＿＿＿＿＿＿＿＿＿＿＿＿＿＿＿＿＿＿＿＿＿＿＿＿＿＿＿＿＿＿

IS THE ESTABLISHMENT LISTED IN LET'S STOP FOR TEA'?　　　　　YES ☐　　NO ☐

NAME OF ESTABLISHMENT:＿＿＿＿＿＿＿＿＿＿＿＿＿＿＿＿＿＿＿＿＿＿＿

ADDRESS:＿＿＿＿＿＿＿＿＿＿＿＿＿＿＿＿＿＿＿＿＿＿＿＿＿＿＿＿＿＿＿

＿＿＿＿＿＿＿＿＿＿＿＿＿＿＿＿＿＿＿＿＿＿＿＿＿＿＿＿＿＿＿＿＿＿＿＿

＿＿＿＿＿＿＿＿＿＿＿＿＿＿＿＿＿＿＿＿＿＿＿＿＿＿＿＿＿＿＿＿＿＿＿＿

YOUR COMMENTS:＿＿＿＿＿＿＿＿＿＿＿＿＿＿＿＿＿＿＿＿＿＿＿＿＿＿＿

＿＿＿＿＿＿＿＿＿＿＿＿＿＿＿＿＿＿＿＿＿＿＿＿＿＿＿＿＿＿＿＿＿＿＿＿

＿＿＿＿＿＿＿＿＿＿＿＿＿＿＿＿＿＿＿＿＿＿＿＿＿＿＿＿＿＿＿＿＿＿＿＿

＿＿＿＿＿＿＿＿＿＿＿＿＿＿＿＿＿＿＿＿＿＿＿＿＿＿＿＿＿＿＿＿＿＿＿＿

＿＿＿＿＿＿＿＿＿＿＿＿＿＿＿＿＿＿＿＿＿＿＿＿＿＿＿＿＿＿＿＿＿＿＿＿

＿＿＿＿＿＿＿＿＿＿＿＿＿＿＿＿＿＿＿＿＿＿＿＿＿＿＿＿＿＿＿＿＿＿＿＿

＿＿＿＿＿＿＿＿＿＿＿＿＿＿＿＿＿＿＿＿＿＿＿＿＿＿＿＿＿＿＿＿＿＿＿＿

Index of Tea Places

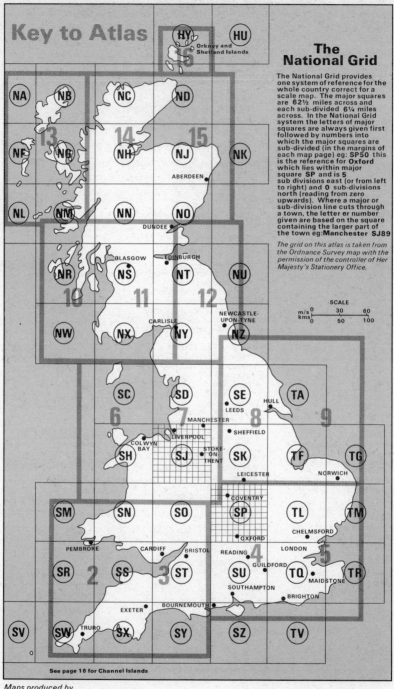

Key to Atlas

Orkney and Shetland Islands

The National Grid

The National Grid provides one system of reference for the whole country correct for a scale map. The major squares are 62½ miles across and each sub-divided 6¼ miles across. In the National Grid system the letters of major squares are always given first followed by numbers into which the major squares are sub-divided (in the margins of each map page) eg: **SP50** this is the reference for **Oxford** which lies within major square **SP** and is **5** sub divisions east (or from left to right) and **0** sub-divisions north (reading from zero upwards). Where a major or sub-division line cuts through a town, the letter or number given are based on the square containing the larger part of the town eg:**Manchester SJ89**

The grid on this atlas is taken from the Ordnance Survey map with the permission of the controller of Her Majesty's Stationery Office.

SCALE

See page 16 for Channel Islands

Maps produced by
The Automobile Association from the
Automaps database.
© The Automobile Association 1990.

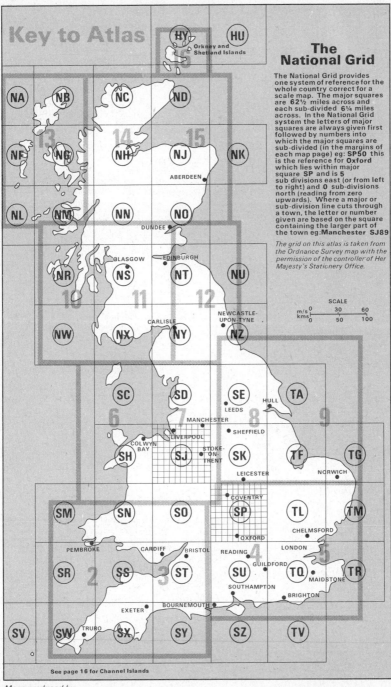

Key to Atlas

Orkney and Shetland Islands

The National Grid

The National Grid provides one system of reference for the whole country correct for a scale map. The major squares are **62½ miles** across and each sub-divided **6¼ miles** across. In the National Grid system the letters of major squares are always given first followed by numbers into which the major squares are sub-divided (in the margins of each map page) eg: **SP50** this is the reference for **Oxford** which lies within major square **SP** and is **5** sub divisions east (or from left to right) and **0** sub-divisions north (reading from zero upwards). Where a major or sub-division line cuts through a town, the letter or number given are based on the square containing the larger part of the town eg: **Manchester SJ89**

The grid on this atlas is taken from the Ordnance Survey map with the permission of the controller of Her Majesty's Stationery Office.

SCALE

HY · HU

NA · NB · NC · ND

NF · NG · NH · NJ · NK
ABERDEEN

NL · NM · NN · NO
DUNDEE

GLASGOW · EDINBURGH

NR · NS · NT · NU

NEWCASTLE-UPON-TYNE

CARLISLE

NW · NX · NY · NZ

SC · SD · SE · TA
LEEDS · HULL

MANCHESTER

LIVERPOOL · SHEFFIELD

COLWYN BAY

SH · SJ · SK · TF · TG
STOKE-ON-TRENT

LEICESTER · NORWICH

COVENTRY

SM · SN · SO · SP · TL · TM
CHELMSFORD

OXFORD

PEMBROKE · CARDIFF · BRISTOL · READING · LONDON

SR · SS · ST · SU · TQ · TR
GUILDFORD · MAIDSTONE

SOUTHAMPTON · BRIGHTON

BOURNEMOUTH

EXETER

SV · SW · SX · SY · SZ · TV
TRURO

See page 16 for Channel Islands

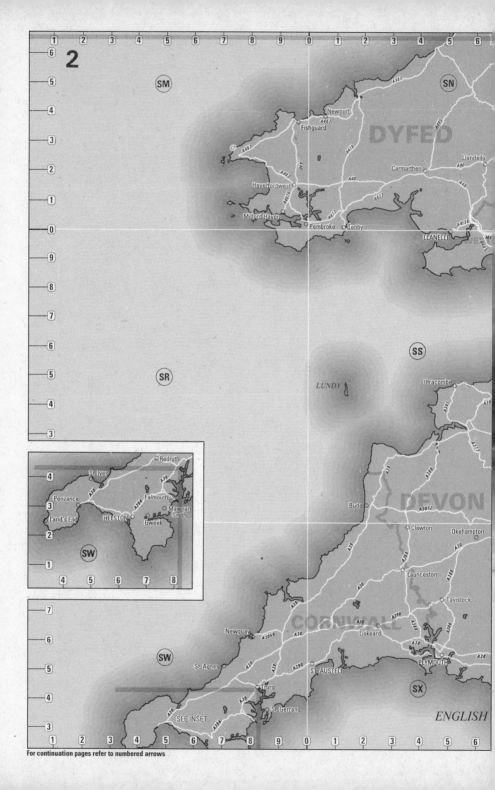

SM

SN

SR

SS

SW

SW

SX

Newport
Fishguard
A487
A487

DYFED

Llandeilo
Carmarthen
A40
A484

Haverfordwest
A40
A477

Milford Haven
Pembroke
Tenby
LLANELLI
M4

LUNDY

Ilfracombe
A361
A39

Bude
A3072

DEVON

Clawton
Okehampton

Launceston
A388
A30
A386

Tavistock

Redruth
St. Ives
A30
A30
Falmouth
Penzance
Mawnan Smith
HELSTON
Land's End
Gweek

Newquay
A3059
A30
A388
A390
Liskeard
A38
A390
St Agnes
A30
A390
St AUSTELL
PLYMOUTH
A38
A38
Truro

CORNWALL

SEE INSET
A394
St Gerrans

ENGLISH

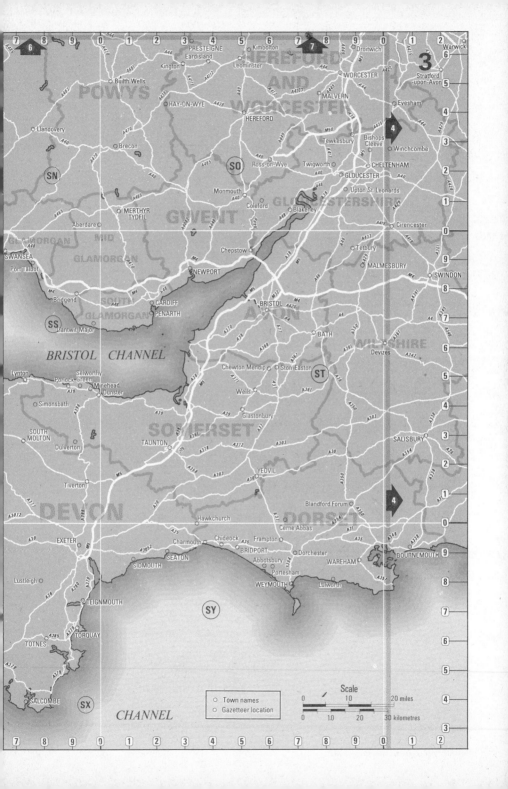

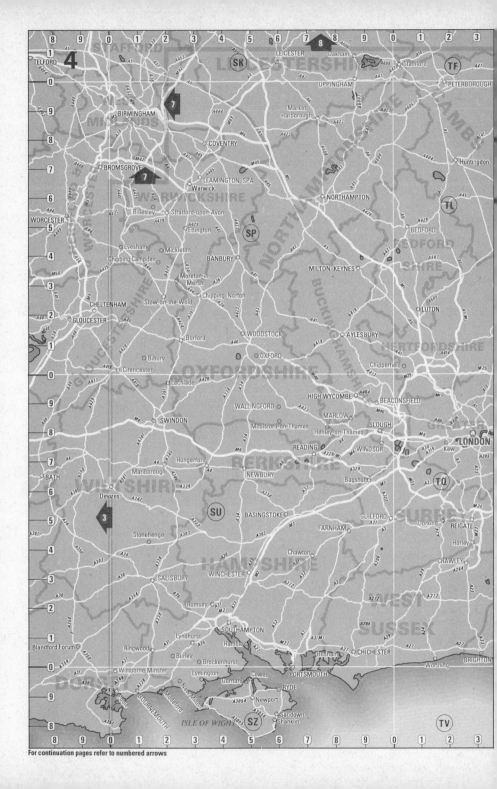

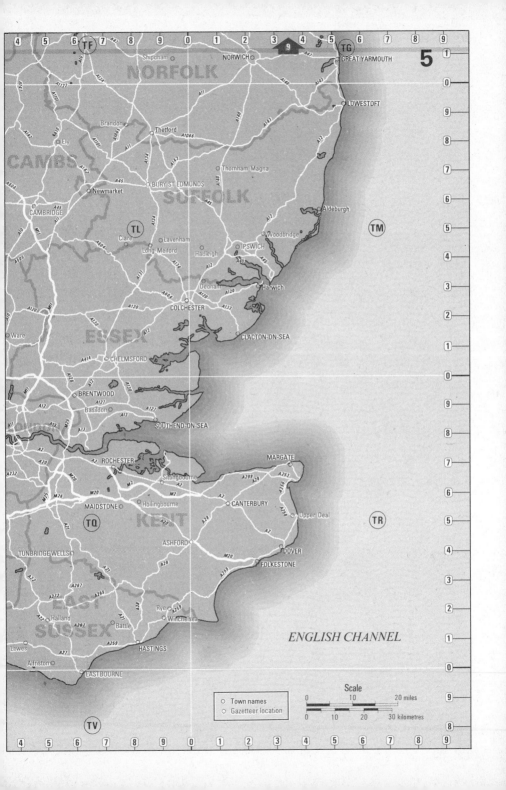

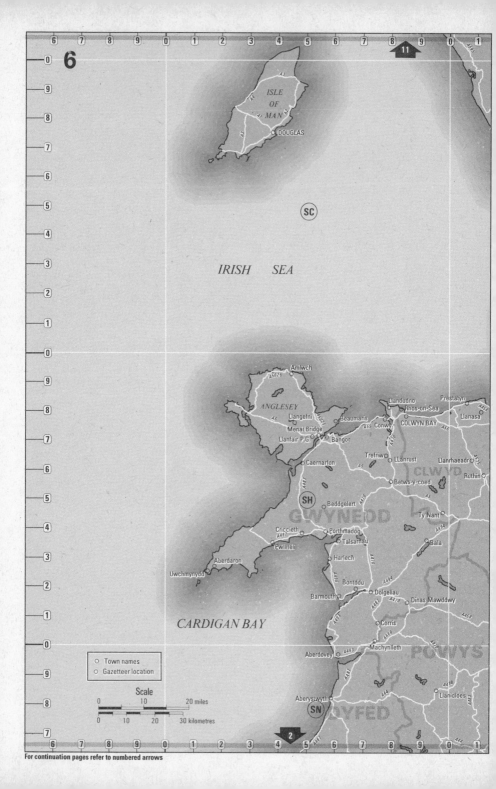

ISLE
OF
MAN

DOUGLAS

SC

IRISH   SEA

Amlwch

ANGLESEY

Llandudno
Rhos-on-Sea
Prestatyn
Llanasa

Llangefni
Beaumaris
Conwy
COLWYN BAY

Menai Bridge
Llanfair P.G
Bangor

Trefriw
Llanrwst
Llanrhaeadr
Ruthin

Caernarfon

CLWYD

Betws-y-coed

SH
Beddgelert

GWYNEDD
Ty Nant

Criccieth
Porthmadog
Bala

Pwllheli
Talsarnau

Aberdaron
Harlech

Uwchmynydd
Bontddu
Dinas Mawddwy

Barmouth
Dolgellau

CARDIGAN BAY
Corris

Aberdovey
Machynlleth
POWYS

○ Town names
○ Gazetteer location

Scale
10
20 miles

0   10   20   30 kilometres

Aberystwyth
Llanidloes

SN
DYFED

11

2

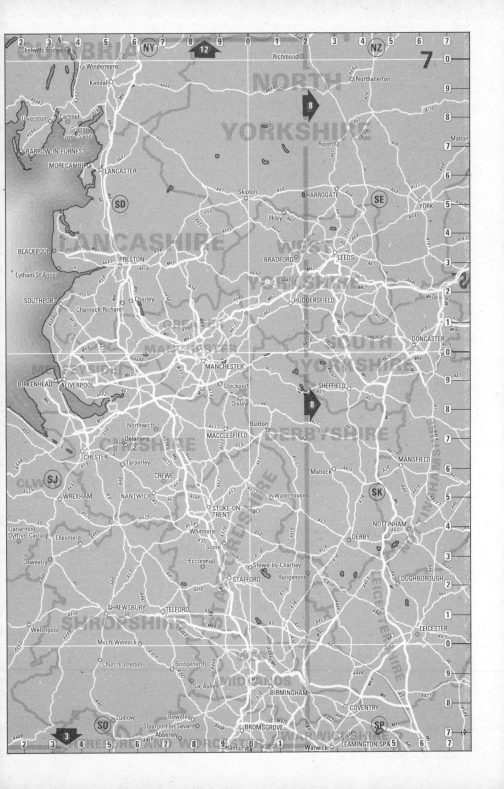

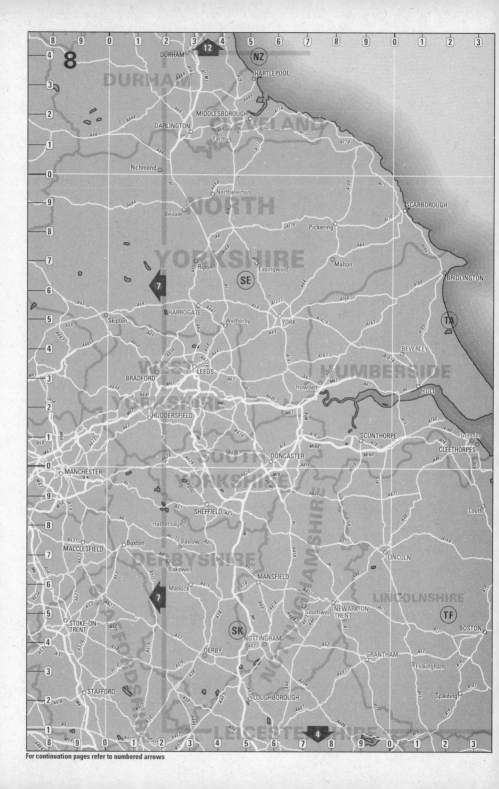

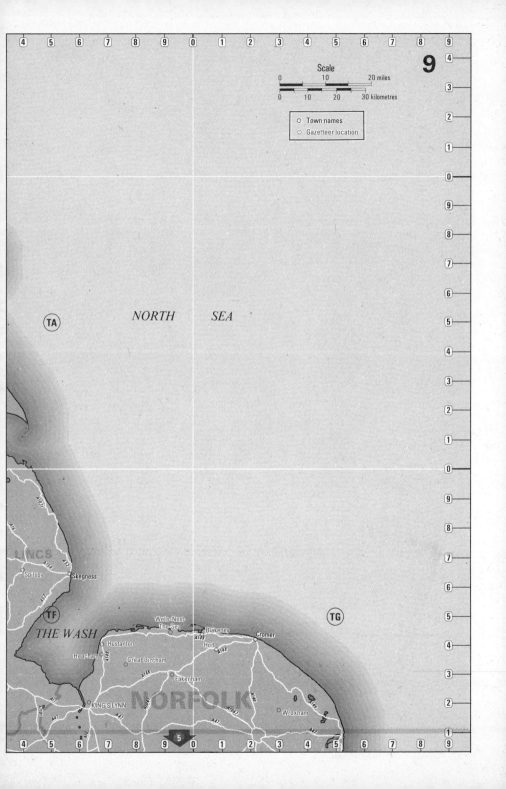

Scale

0   10   20 miles

0   10   20   30 kilometres

○ Town names
○ Gazetteer location

TA

NORTH   SEA

LINCS

Spilsby   Skegness

TF

TG

THE WASH

Wells-Next-
The-Sea   Blakeney   Cromer

A149

Hunstanton   Holt

Heacham   A149

Great Bircham

A148

Fakenham

NORFOLK

KING'S LYNN   Wroxham

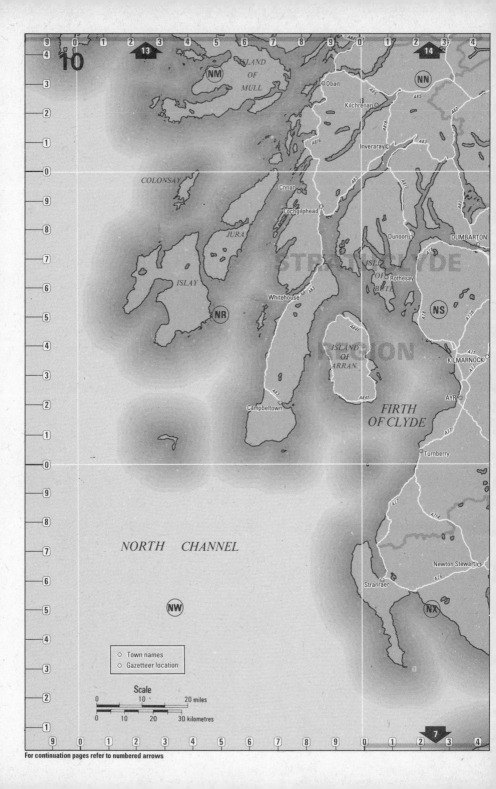

ISLAND
OF
MULL

NM

Oban
Kilchrenan

Inveraray

COLONSAY

Crnan

Lochgilphead

JURA

Dunoon
DUMBARTON

ISLAY

Whitehouse

ISLE
OF
BUTE

Rothesay

NR

NS

ISLAND
OF
ARRAN

KILMARNOCK

AYR

FIRTH
OF CLYDE

Campbeltown

Turnberry

NORTH   CHANNEL

NW

Newton Stewart

Stranraer

NX

○ Town names
○ Gazetteer location

Scale

0   10   20 miles

0   10   20   30 kilometres

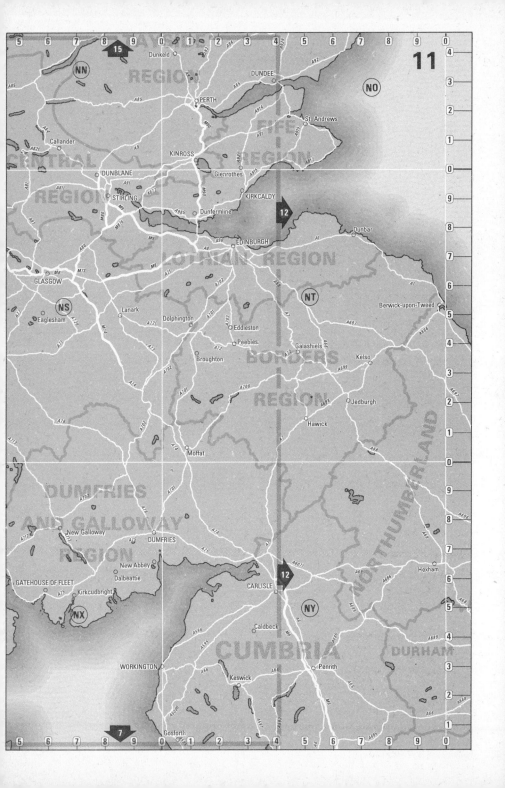

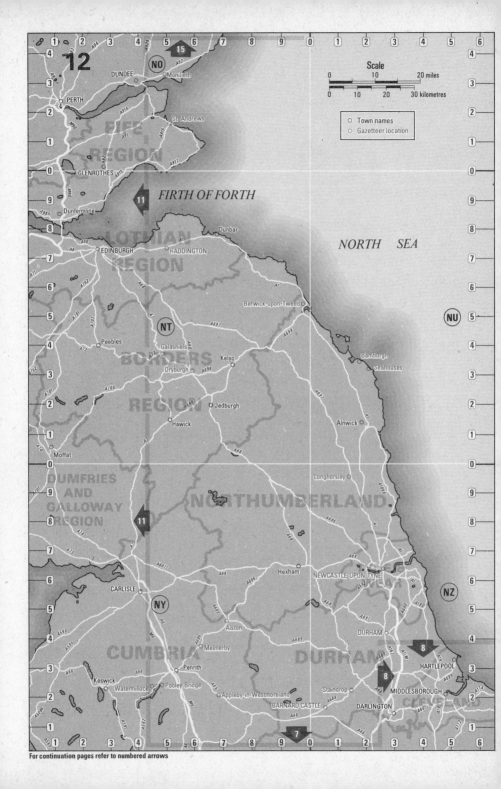

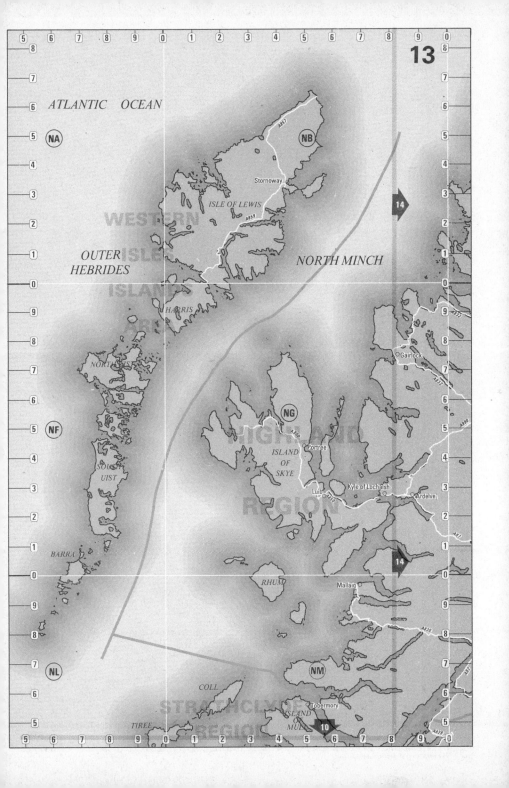

ATLANTIC   OCEAN

NA

NB

Stornoway

ISLE OF LEWIS

A857

A859

WESTERN   ISLES

ISLANDS

OUTER
HEBRIDES

NORTH MINCH

14

HARRIS

NORTH UIST

NF

NG

Gairlock

A877

HIGHLAND

Portree

A890

ISLAND
OF
SKYE

Kyle of Lochalsh

Ardelve

SOUTH
UIST

Luib

A851

REGION

A87

BARRA

14

RHUM

Mallaig

A830

NL

NM

A87

COLL

Tobermory

STRATHCLYDE

TIREE

ISLAND
OF MULL

10

REGION

A828

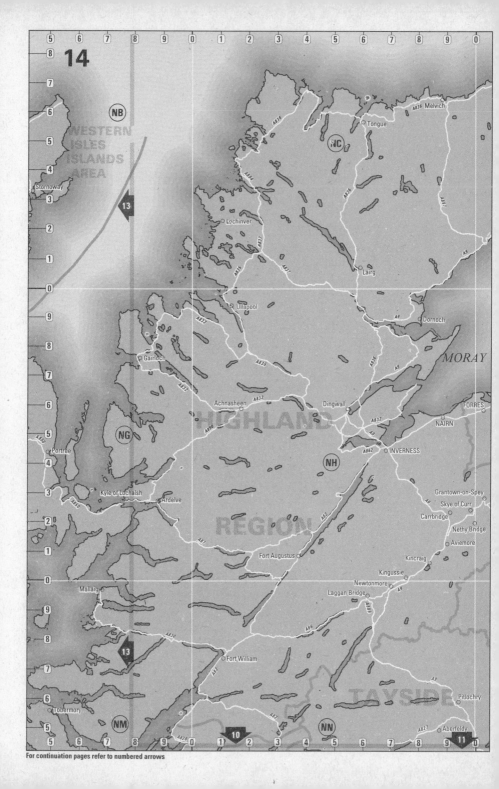

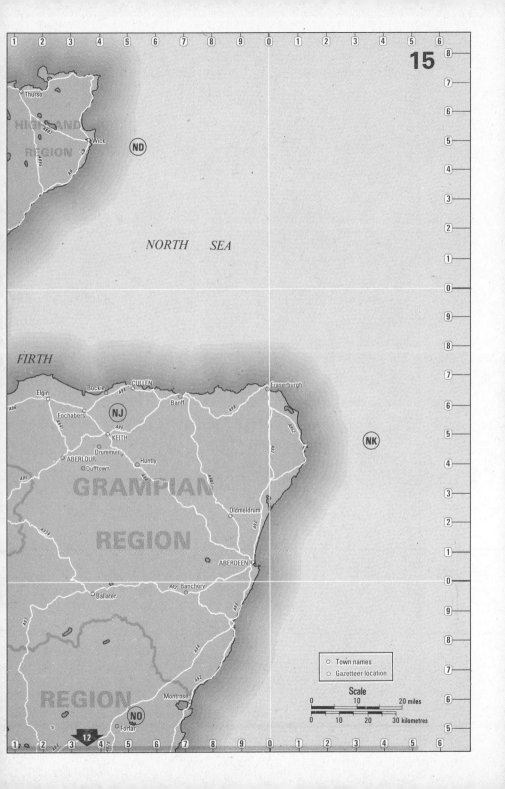

NORTH SEA

FIRTH

Thurso

Wick

ND

Elgin
Buckie
CULLEN
Fraserburgh
Fochabers
Banff
NJ
KEITH
Drummuir
ABERLOUR
Huntly
Dufftown

NK

GRAMPIAN

Oldmeldrum

REGION

ABERDEEN

Ballater
Banchory

REGION

Montrose

NO

Fortar

○ Town names
○ Gazetteer location

Scale

0   10   20 miles

0   10   20   30 kilometres

12

16

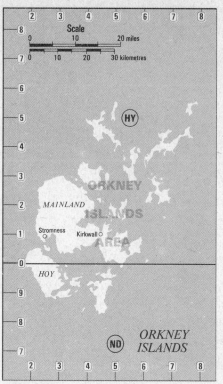

Scale
0 10 20 miles
0 10 20 30 kilometres

HY

ORKNEY
ISLANDS
AREA

MAINLAND

Stromness ○
Kirkwall ○

HOY

ND

*ORKNEY
ISLANDS*

Scale
0 10 20 miles
0 10 20 30 kilometres

HP

YELL

SHETLAND
ISLANDS
AREA

MAINLAND

HU

Lerwick ○

*SHETLAND
ISLANDS*

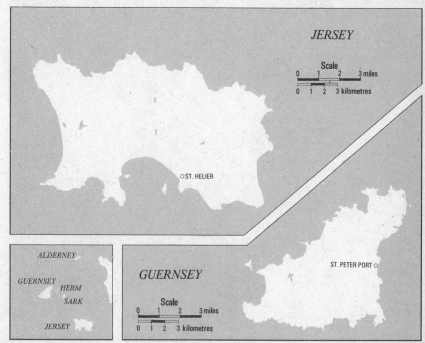

JERSEY

Scale
0 1 2 3 miles
0 1 2 3 kilometres

○ ST. HELIER

ALDERNEY

GUERNSEY

HERM

SARK

JERSEY

GUERNSEY

ST. PETER PORT ○

Scale
0 1 2 3 miles
0 1 2 3 kilometres